The Open University
Technology
A Third Level Course

Unit 15 ARTIFICIAL INTELLIGENCE, EXPERT SYSTEMS AND CAD

Prepared for the Course Team
by Philip Steadman

T363 COMPUTER AIDED DESIGN

The Open University

THE COMPUTER AIDED DESIGN COURSE TEAM (1990)

Academics Ray Matela (Chairman)
Nigel Cross
Jeff Johnson
Joe Rooney
Philip Steadman

Consultant Chris Denham

Academic Computing Gerry Cooper
Ian Every

BBC Producer Phil Ashby

Course Manager Christopher Pym

Editor Garry Hammond

Graphic Designer Rob Williams

Graphic Artist John Taylor

Secretaries Jennifer Conlon
Carole Marshall
Pat Prince

The Open University, Walton Hall, Milton Keynes MK7 6AA

Designed by the Graphic Design Group of the Open University.

Filmset in Great Britain by Santype International Ltd., Salisbury, Wilts.

Printed and bound in the United Kingdom by Staples Printers Rochester Limited, Neptune Close, Medway City Estate, Frindsbury, Rochester, Kent ME2 4LT.

This text is one component of a multi-media Open University Third Level Course. For general availability of course materials, please write to: Open University Educational Enterprises, 12 Cofferidge Close, Stony Stratford, Milton Keynes MK11 1BY, Great Britain.

First published 1987. Second edition 1991. Reprinted 1993.

ISBN 07492 60572
Edition 2.2

CONTENTS

INTRODUCTION

In the introduction to the Course Textbook, *Principles of Computer-Aided Design*, the authors argue that most current commercial CAD systems serve the later stages of the design process. They provide tools for draughting, modelling and analysis; but all these are brought into use once a design is fairly well worked-out, and only the details remain to be resolved. So far there have been relatively few computer aids to the early, conceptual stages of design; few 'draughting systems' intended for sketching as opposed to the production of working drawings; few successful programs for the automated synthesis of design solutions (systems for electronic circuit layout being a notable exception).

CAD researchers however have been turning their attention in the 1980s and 1990s to the earlier, more creative parts of the design process. They are looking at ways in which computer programs might aid the imaginative thought processes of designers, or how programs might be constructed so as to codify and encapsulate the expert knowledge which designers possess. Such concerns have taken them into those fields of computer science and human psychology which have become known as 'artificial intelligence' (AI) research. Already a few of the types of program termed 'expert systems' have been developed for real-world design applications.

In this Unit we have brought together some journal articles and extracts from books, to give an indication of what is going on in the field of artificial intelligence and expert systems. This is a fast-developing subject, and the only way to keep abreast of current developments is by reading the research journals.

The selection of papers and extracts in this Unit will be changed from time to time as the field develops. Obviously in a small space we can give only a very partial and fragmentary view. So we have concentrated on some introductory ideas, plus descriptions of two representative examples of expert systems for design, one a prototype, one in actual use.

The intelligent computer

The first selection is from Patrick Winston's book *Artificial Intelligence*, which has come to be regarded as a classic since its first publication in 1981. The book gives a comprehensive account of the theoretical ideas behind AI work in many fields — language, vision, learning, common-sense knowledge and human problem-solving — in a style which is clear and straightforward, without technicalities or jargon. (For any person wanting to learn about AI generally, it is a very good place to start.) We reprint here extracts from the first chapter, in which Winston surveys the range of things that computers can do now, and might do in the near future.

There has been much controversy about exactly what the term 'artificial intelligence' should mean (and indeed about whether computers can be said to display intelligence at all). Winston gives his own definition of AI, which is "the study of ideas that enable computers to be intelligent". As he says, this definition implies two main aims for AI research. The first is to increase knowledge about how intelligence is possible in humans and in machines. In this sense then, AI falls within the scope of the academic discipline of psychology. The second is to make computers more useful. In the commercial CAD world, AI applications are usually discussed in this second, instrumental context — as leading to more 'intelligent' computer programs.

But, as Winston emphasizes, this is not the only way in which AI could prove in the longer run to be of practical usefulness. If AI research were, in time, to throw light on the mental processes of designers and the nature of human problem-solving methods in design, then this might lead to improvements in the education of designers themselves. In Winston's words, "the methodology involved in making smart programs may transfer to making smart people".

Expert systems in CAD

Our second selection is an editorial article in the journal *Computer-Aided Design* by architectural researcher John Gero. It introduces the subfield of artificial intelligence known as 'knowledge engineering' — that is, "the art of building complex computer programs that represent and reason with knowledge of the world". 'Expert systems' are programs of this type. They have been defined as "intelligent computer programs which use symbolic inference procedures to deal with problems that are difficult enough to require significant human expertise for their solution". Gero explains with a simple example what is meant here by 'symbolic inference procedures'; and he describes the basic components from which expert systems are made up.

Expert systems differ from conventional programs in that the knowledge they embody can be added to in a piecewise fashion. The expert system goes through a process of reasoning, or inference, drawing on this 'knowledge base'. The reasoning may be based on partial knowledge, and may be of a probabilistic nature, like much human reasoning — as compared with the deterministic and strictly deductive character of most conventional programs. Many expert systems are capable of giving some explanation of the basis for their calculations or deductions, and a description of the processes of inference by which those conclusions were reached. A section of the CADPAC 7 text is devoted to expert systems; you might wish to study that part of the CADPAC software at this point.

Problem-solving paradigms

In our third selection we return to Winston's book *Artificial Intelligence*, Chapter 6, to look at problem-solving paradigms in AI which are especially relevant to design. The first is the *generate-and-test* paradigm with which Herbert Simon's name is particularly associated. You will remember that Simon was quoted in this connection in Section 2 of the introduction to *Principles of Computer-Aided Design*. The first example which Winston describes in detail may at first seem remote from design, but it is actually one which has excited some interest among CAD researchers. This is the DENDRAL expert system for chemical analysis, on which development started as long ago as 1965. The reason is that DENDRAL is rather suggestive for the design process, since it consists of a generating part and a testing or analysis part; and, more specifically, the potential 'solutions' which it generates are three-dimensional geometrical structures, i.e. possible configurations for organic molecules. It is also of interest because the generator enumerates *all possible* molecular structures (all 'designs') which satisfy the given chemical formula (the 'brief' or 'design constraints').

Winston then moves on to *rule-based synthesis systems*. The general ideas are introduced through the example of a 'toy system' called BAGGER whose function is to drive a robot packing grocery bags in a supermarket. CADPAC 7 gives you the opportunity to experiment for yourself with an implementation of BAGGER (refer to the relevant sub-section of the CADPAC 7 text). BAGGER decides the order for putting purchases in bags, and its 'intelligence' or 'expertise' consists in such things as packing large bottles by preference at the bottom of the bag, putting frozen items in an insulated bag, and so on. In a *very* liberal interpretation then, BAGGER could be described as a 'design system' — for 'designing' arrangements of groceries in bags. It serves to demonstrate the principles behind the first commercially successful expert system for engineering design, broadly interpreted: that is the XCON system which designs layouts or configurations for Digital Equipment Corporation computer installations. XCON was developed in the late 1970s and remained until the late 1980s one of the few expert systems for design in everyday practical use.

AI-based design versus geometry-based design

In the fourth selection we reproduce a paper by Tim Smithers from *Computer Aided Design* journal which reviews a whole range of present and possible future AI applications in mechanical engineering, architectural design and electronics design. Not the least of the merits of this paper is that it contains a lengthy bibliography of representative papers in these fields.

Smithers's main argument is that existing commercial CAD tools are inadequate for supporting anything but a small part of the activities in which a designer engages. He reviews briefly the history of computer draughting and modelling, covering many of the same points as the Introduction to the Course Textbook. Much of the knowledge which the designer brings to bear in design and generates during the design process, he says, cannot be directly or simply related to the geometric form of the artefact; and in any case this geometric form is the *outcome* of the process, the resolution of the constraints to be satisfied, and not the starting point. It follows that attempts to *extend* geometric models (or 'decorate' them in Smithers's word) to support representations of these other kinds of knowledge are largely misguided. Other forms of *knowledge representation* are needed which are more suited to the many different types of knowledge used in design.

Smithers goes on to survey research into AI-based design during the 1980s. Early work was directed at some well-defined design problems such as circuit layout in which constraints and requirements can be expressed with mathematical precision. A large *solution space* of combinatorial possibilities is thus generated, and can be searched systematically. Some of the principles of automated search processes are covered in the 'Automatic design synthesis' section of the CADPAC 7 text. More recent research into AI-based design has concentrated on three areas: techniques for representing and reasoning about design knowledge; improved models of the design process itself; and integrated software system architectures required for AI-based design tools.

Smithers sets out a model of the engineering design process, consisting of a list of the activities undertaken, in broadly chronological sequence — although he recognizes that many activities will be repeated, and intuitive leaps made from one activity to another. He then asks the question 'What kinds of support might computer aids give to these various activities?' and lists four answers: knowledge representation; mundane or laborious levels of reasoning; maintaining the consistency of the knowledge generated; and control of the design process. Each area is discussed in more detail, with examples.

The kinds of knowledge employed in the early stages of the mechanical engineering design process, which might be represented formally in the software, could for example include knowledge of the mechanisms to be used, types and properties of materials, ranges of performance parameters, as well as some geometrical aspects — none of which, including the geometrical knowledge at this stage, can be represented using a conventional solid modeller.

Automated reasoning techniques could be used to support the relatively well-defined areas of detail design and the sizing of components, as for example the dimensioning of shafts and bearings illustrated by Smithers. Conflicts between design requirements could be detected automatically, and logical consistency maintained in the description of the emerging design or designs. Techniques for drawing logical inferences through *forward chaining* and *backward chaining* are explained in more detail in CADPAC 7, in the sub-section on 'General architectures for expert systems'.

Finally, computers might be employed in the control of systems to support the design process. A system should be able to decide which of various subsystems to bring into action at any stage; it should be able to maintain consistency in the descriptions of designs, and as a consequence it should be able to take an active role in aiding the designer, rather than just providing a passive tool. However, these desirable properties have not yet been realized in actual working systems, and remain topics for research.

Norema Design: a knowledge based system for kitchen design

The next paper describes an example, in terms of Smithers's categories, of automated reasoning or inferencing techniques applied to that very familiar area of architectural design, the layout of kitchens. 'Norema Design' is unusual in being not a prototype or research program, but a working expert system in practical everyday use. It is a development and extension of the kinds of commercial kitchen planning aids mentioned in the CADPAC 2 text. A simple 'unintelligent' draughting and/or modelling package for kitchen layout must be used by a professional designer to give the best results. 'Norema Design' aims to encapsulate this expertise which the professional brings to bear, and to make it available to sales staff and members of the general public.

The system accepts the plan outline of the user's kitchen. It then selects 'modules' (cabinets, pieces of equipment, etc.) and places them within the kitchen, under various functional constraints (access, plumbing, safety etc.), like those built into the CADPAC kitchen planning software, as well as further constraints determined by the client's tastes and preferences. The functional constraints are expressed as rules of an *If–Then* type, and were elicited from professional designers in a series of interviews.

The design process goes through four stages. At the first stage the outline plan of the kitchen is input. Next, zones are established, principally around the walls of the room (although 'peninsulas' are also allowed) in which the required modules can be placed. Some general placement constraints are taken into account at this stage, such as that units must not obstruct door swings, wall cabinets must not obstruct windows, and so on. At the third stage the modules required within the kitchen are selected from a library and positioned in the allowable zones (the 'configuration task'). There may be open spaces left temporarily (or permanently) between modules. The modules and open spaces occurring within a partial design solution are represented by means of an hierarchical classification referred to as an 'IS-A taxonomy'. Thus a module IS A 'design entity', and an open space also IS A 'design entity' (see Figure 6).

Rules of an *If–Then* type are applied in the selection of modules. Some modules can also be selected directly by the user. Modules are categorized into different types and introduced into the plan in a corresponding sequence.

In the configuration task, the modules are placed in all possible alternative positions, and these positions ranked according to specified rules. If no acceptable position is found, then some of the constraints may be relaxed (others are absolute); or else the attempt to place the module is abandoned. The paper gives a worked example showing how modules are shuffled along one 'arm' of the layout in order to introduce a new module, and the relevant functional and dimensional constraints tested.

Some of the procedures for placement are described as *heuristics*: that is to say they will tend, but are not guaranteed, to lead to the desired result (as distinct from algorithms which if correctly applied have a guaranteed outcome). These heuristics, and the careful control of the order in which modules are placed, have the effect of greatly reducing the size of the solution spaces to be searched. This point is demonstrated in the 'automatic kitchen design' exercises in CADPAC 7. However, as the authors of the paper say, the consequence is that 'Norema Design' does not produce layouts which are 'optimal' even within the system's own criteria — only 'functionally good' solutions which can then be modified interactively by the user.

An expert system for preliminary numerical design modelling

The final paper by MacCallum and Duffy describes the DESIGNER system in the context of applications in naval architecture. In contrast with the detailed layout concerns of the previous paper, MacCallum and Duffy concentrate on the broad overall decisions made in the very preliminary, conceptual stages of the whole design process: in this case decisions about such general parameters of a ship's design as its length, beam, draught, weight, speed and power.

The authors argue that at this stage designers construct mental models of the object being designed and its behaviour. Different models abstract different characteristics and different relationships between those characteristics. MacCallum and Duffy's system is intended to allow designers to make the structure of these models explicit, and to explore their implications.

DESIGNER allows the user to build such a structure in the form of a directed network (a graph with directions, indicated by arrows, on the edges). The nodes or vertices represent characteristics of the design (length, weight, etc.), and each directed edge represents the fact that one characteristic is dependent in some way on another. These relationships might be known from physical laws, or even by definition (e.g. the volume of a box is dependent on length, breadth and depth). Other relationships might be based on empirical knowledge, and might be only approximately expressed.

The system allows the designer to trace the influence of different factors one on another, to examine the strength of such influences through what may well be a complex web of inter-relationships, and to determine numerical values for selected characteristics — or ranges of values within specified bounds of accuracy — given certain fixed values for other characteristics. Thus in the worked example the required deadweight and trial speed of the vessel are given, and the main dimensions of length, beam, draught, etc. are to be determined.

One shortcoming of this approach is that it deals with simple numerically expressed relations only, and not directly with spatial arrangements as such. It is also dependent of course on designers having a fair understanding of the typical pairwise relationships between the chosen characteristics of those classes of designed objects with which they are dealing.

ACKNOWLEDGEMENTS

Grateful acknowledgement is made to the following sources for permission to use material in this unit:

Text

Winston, P. H. *Artificial Intelligence*, 2nd edn, Chapters 1 and 6 (excerpts) © 1984, Addison-Wesley Publishing Company, Inc., Reading Massachusetts; Gero, J. 'Expert systems in CAD', *Computer Aided Design*, November 1985, Butterworth & Co. (Publishers) Ltd; Kloster, M., Gjerløw, J. C. and Ohren, O. 'Norema design: a knowledge based system for kitchen design', in Gero, J. S. (ed.) *Artificial Intelligence in Design*, 1989, Springer Verlag; Smithers, T. 'AI-based design versus geometry-based design, or Why design cannot be supported by geometry alone', *Computer Aided Design*, Vol. 21, No. 3, April 1989, Butterworth & Co. (Publishers) Ltd; MacCallum, K. J. and Duffy, A. 'An expert system for preliminary numerical design modelling', in the conference proceedings of *Advances in Engineering Software*, 1985, Springer Verlag.

Figures

'The intelligent computer': *Figure 1*: Forbus, K. D., University of Illinois; *Figure 2:* adapted from Sussman, G. J. and Stallman, R. M. (1975) 'Heuristic techniques in computer aided circuit analysis', *IEEE Transactions on Circuits and Systems*, Vol. CAS-22, No. 11, November 1975, copyright © 1975 by the Institute of Electrical and Electronic Engineers; *Figure 3:* Stallman, R. M. and Sussman, G. J. 'Forward reasoning and dependency backtracking', *Artificial Intelligence*, Vol. 9, No. 2, 1977, North-Holland Publishing Co.; *Figure 4:* adapted from Winston, P. H. (ed.) (1975) *The Psychology of Computer Vision*, copyright © 1975 by McGraw-Hill Book Co,; *Figures 5 and 6:* Grimson, W. E. L. *From Images to Surfaces*, (1981), MIT Press; *Figure 10:* Michalski, R. S., University of Illinois.

Extracts from Chapter 1 of *Artificial Intelligence*, by P. H. Winston

THE INTELLIGENT COMPUTER

There are many ways to define the field of Artificial Intelligence. Here is one:

- Artificial Intelligence is the study of ideas that enable computers to be intelligent.

But what is intelligence? Is it the ability to reason? Is it the ability to acquire and apply knowledge? Is it the ability to perceive and manipulate things in the physical world? Surely all of these abilities are part of what intelligence is, but they are not the whole of what can be said. A definition in the usual sense seems impossible because intelligence appears to be an amalgam of so many information-representation and information-processing talents.

Nevertheless, the goals of the field of Artificial Intelligence can be defined as follows:

- One central goal of Artificial Intelligence is to make computers more useful.
- Another central goal is to understand the principles that make intelligence possible.

[...]

Making Computers Intelligent Helps Us Understand Intelligence

The perspective of Artificial Intelligence complements the traditional perspectives of psychology, linguistics, and philosophy. Here are some reasons why:

- Computer metaphors aid thinking. Work with computers has led to a rich new language for talking about how to do things and how to describe things. Metaphorical and analogical use of the concepts involved enables more powerful thinking about thinking.
- Computer models force precision. Implementing a theory uncovers conceptual mistakes and oversights that ordinarily escape even the most meticulous researchers. Major roadblocks often appear that were not recognized as problems at all before beginning the cycle of thinking and experimenting.
- Computer implementations quantify task requirements. Once a program performs a task, upper-bound statements can be made about how much information processing the task requires.
- Computer programs exhibit unlimited patience, they require no feeding, and they do not bite. Moreover, it is usually simple to deprive a computer program of some piece of knowledge in order to test how important that piece really is. It is impossible to work with animal brains with the same precision

Note that wanting to make computers *be* intelligent is not the same as wanting to make computers *simulate* intelligence. Artificial Intelligence excites people who want to uncover principles that all intelligent information processors must exploit, not just those made of wet neural tissue instead of dry electronics. Consequently, there is neither an obsession with mimicking human intelligence nor a prejudice against using methods that seem involved in human intelligence. Instead, there is a new point of view that brings along a new methodology and leads to new theories.

One result of this new point of view may be new ideas about how to help people become more intelligent. Just as psychological knowledge about human information processing can help make computers intelligent, theories derived purely with computers in mind often suggest possibilities about methods to educate people better. Said another way, the methodology involved in making smart programs may transfer to making smart people.

Intelligent Computers Are More Useful Computers

Do we really need to make our computers smarter? It seems so. As the world grows more complex, we must use our energy, food, and human resources wisely, and we must have high-quality help from computers to do it. Computers must help not only by doing ordinary computing, but also by doing computing that exhibits intelligence.

It is easy to think of amazing applications for intelligent computers, many of which seem like science fiction by yesterday's standards. Here are a few:

- In business, computers should suggest financial strategies and give marketing advice. Moreover, computers should schedule people and groups, refer problems to the right people, summarize news, and polish draft documents, freeing them of grammatical errors.
- In engineering, computers should check design rules, recall relevant precedent designs, offer suggestions, and otherwise help create new products.
- In manufacturing, computers should do the dangerous and boring assembly, inspection, and maintenance jobs.
- In farming, computers should control pests, prune trees, and selectively harvest mixed crops.
- In mining, computers should work where the conditions are too dangerous for people, and they should recover the manganese nodules from the bottom of the sea.
- In schools, computers should understand their students' mistakes, not just react to them. Computers should act as superbooks in which microprocessors display orbiting planets and play musical scores.
- In hospitals, computers should help with diagnosis, monitor patients' conditions, manage treatment, and make beds.
- In households, computers should give advice on cooking and shopping, clean the floors, mow the lawn, do the laundry, and deal with maintenance.

Some of these things are being done now. Others are close. Still others will require a lot more work. All are possible.

[...]

WHAT COMPUTERS CAN DO

[Let] us look at some representative examples of what computers can do once they are programmed.... Be cautious, however! It is as easy to become a rabid believer as it is to remain dogmatically pessimistic. Much remains to be discovered, and when talking about what computers can do, it is often appropriate to preface claims with, "To some extent... ." In most cases, basic research is only now becoming engineering practice.

Computers Can Solve Difficult Problems

An early program, written by James R. Slagle, operated in the world of integral calculus. Computers can do arithmetic at unbelievable speed, of course. Slagle showed they can do much more, accepting integration problems and producing answers like this:

$$\int \frac{x^4}{(1-x^2)^{5/2}}\,dx = \sin^{-1} x - \tan(\sin^{-1} x) + \frac{1}{3}\tan^3(\sin^{-1} x)$$

Slagle's program is simple enough to serve as a programming example even though it comfortably handles problems from university-level examinations. Subsequent programs, like one by Joel Moses in the MACSYMA system, do even better because they have more and better knowledge. No human can compete with them.

Much more recently, programs have been written that solve mechanical problems. Faced with the spring-loaded reducer valve in Figure 1, a program by Kenneth D. Forbus produces the following explanation for what happens when the pressure rises in the output port:

What happens when...

When the pressure in the output port, Out, rises, the increasing pressure pushes the diaphragm, D, up and closes the auxiliary valve, A. The pressure in the auxiliary valve's output chamber falls, the pressure in the piston steam port falls, and the piston moves up and closes the main valve. The pressure in the main valve's

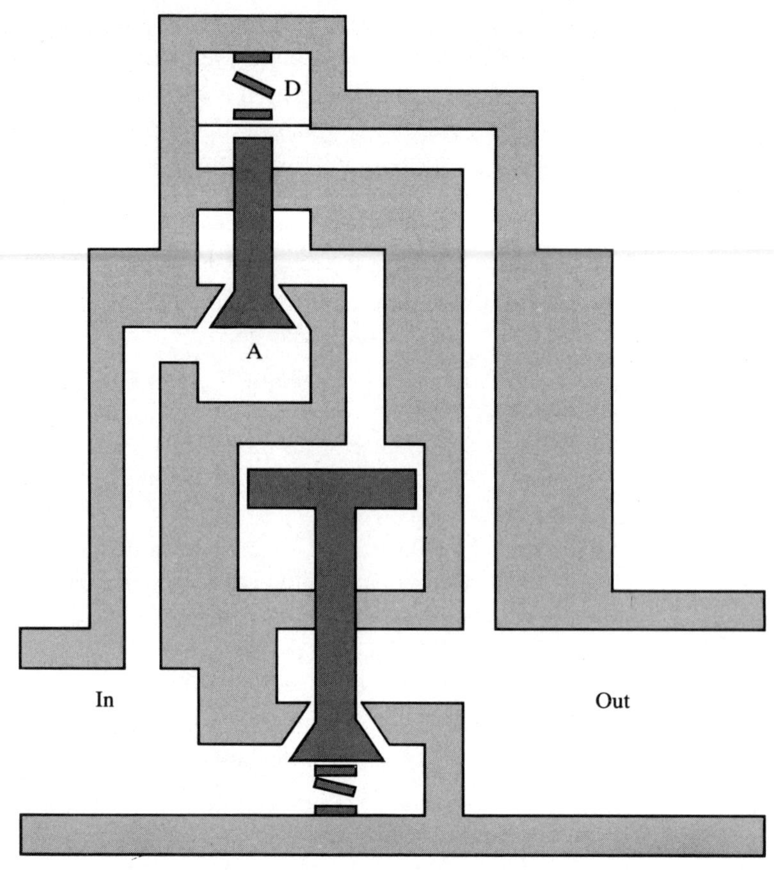

Figure 1 A spring-loaded reducer valve that reduces high-pressure steam at 1200 psi to low-pressure steam at a constant pressure of 12 psi. A program can explain how such mechanisms work. Courtesy of Kenneth D. Forbus.

output chamber falls, causing the pressure in the output port to fall. Note that when the pressure in the output port rises, it causes the system to act so that the pressure in the output port falls. This means the system exhibits negative feedback.

Computers Can Help Experts Analyze and Design

Some programs are intended to help physicians analyze certain kinds of disease. One, MYCIN, by Edward Shortliffe, specializes in certain bacterial infections. Another, CADUCEUS, by Harry E. Pople, Jr. and Jack D. Myers is for internal medicine. The performance of both programs is moving toward the level of human specialists.

Another powerful analysis program, by Gerald J. Sussman and Richard M. Stallman, is for understanding electronic circuits. Their program, EL, reaches conclusions about a diagram like the one in Figure 2, using humanlike reasoning, rather than brute-force attack on the network equations. An advantage lies in the system's ability to talk about what it has done in terms human engineers can understand.

Another analysis program, PROSPECTOR, developed by Richard O. Duda, Peter E. Hart, and Rene Reboh, helped to discover a promising new extension to an existing molybdenum deposit near Mount Tolman in Washington.

Programs for analysis are complemented by others for engineering design. Figure 3 shows an integrated-circuit chip designed with help from a program. Another representative design program used in the computer business is XCON, originally called R1, developed cooperatively by John McDermott at Carnegie-Mellon University, Arnold Kraft and Dennis O'Connor at the Digital Equipment Corporation, and their associates. XCON decides how to configure the various modules in a computer system.

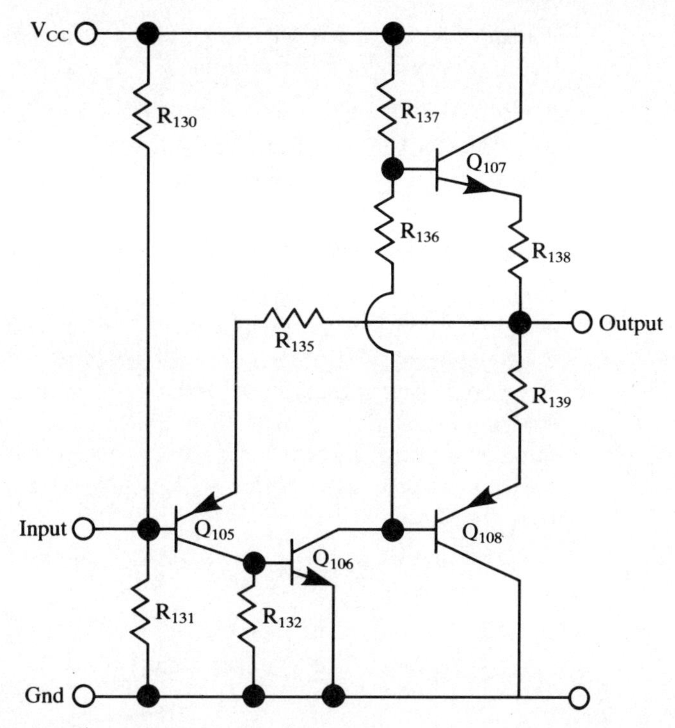

Figure 2 Circuit-understanding programs use humanlike reasoning to determine network voltages and currents. They explain complicated electronic devices in terms that are understood easily by electrical engineers. Adapted from "Heuristic Techniques in Computer Aided Circuit Analysis," by Gerald J. Sussman and Richard M. Stallman, *IEEE Transactions on Circuits and Systems*, vol. CAS-22, no. 11, November, 1975, copyright 1975 by the Institute of Electrical and Electronics Engineers, New York.

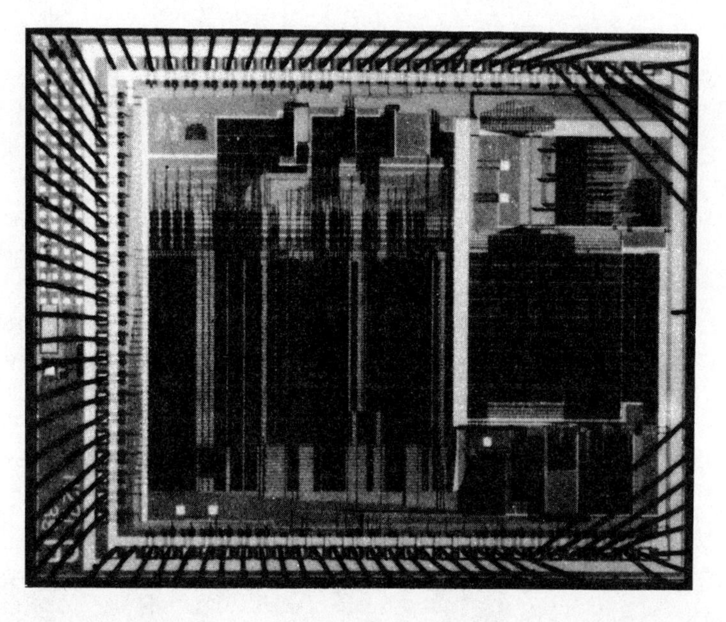

Figure 3 An integrated circuit designed with the help of an intelligent program. Courtesy of John Batali, Edmond Goodhue, Christopher Hanson, Howard E. Shrobe, Richard M. Stallman, and Gerald J. Sussman.

Computers Can Understand Simple English

There are now several programs that are capable of handling questions expressed in English. One of these, INTELLECT, developed by Larry R. Harris, answers English questions like the following:

- I wonder how actual sales for last month compared to the forecasts for people under quota in New England?

Another program, LIFER, developed by Gary G. Hendrix, was originally specialized to answering questions in the world of ships:

- How many Spruance class ships are there?
- Who is the captain of the Kennedy?
- What is the length of Old Ironsides?

Computers Can Understand Simple Images

Equipped with television cameras, computers can see well enough to deal with certain limited worlds. From drawings of a blocks world, for example, they make conclusions about what kinds of objects are present, what relations exist between them, and what groups they form. A program by David Waltz notes that the line drawing in Figure 4 depicts eight objects, including three that form an arch in the middle foreground. It further observes that to the left of the arch is a wedge, and to the right is a distorted brick with a hole, and a three-object tower stands in the background.

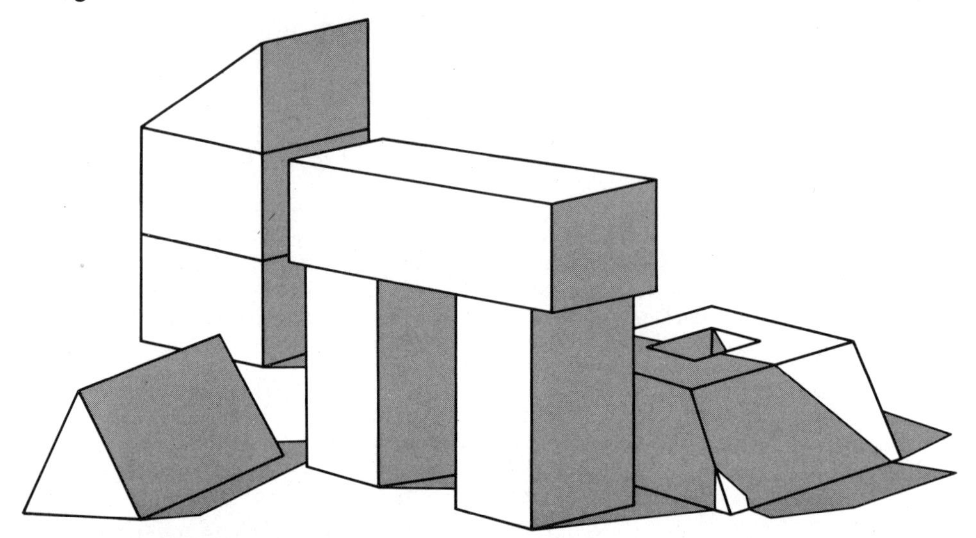

Figure 4 A drawing-understanding program uses knowledge about possible vertex configurations to analyze lines. Typical drawings have cracks, shadows, boundaries, concave lines, and convex lines. Adapted from *The Psychology of Computer Vision*, edited by Patrick H. Winston, copyright 1975 by McGraw-Hill Book Company, New York.

Unfortunately, it is much harder to work with images from a camera than to work with prepared drawings. Promising progress has been made, nevertheless. Figure 5, for example, shows a pair of aerial images, and Figure 6 shows a contour map produced from the images using two procedures: a binocular stereo procedure based on the ideas of David Marr, Tomaso Poggio, and W. Eric L. Grimson: and a surface-reconstruction procedure based on the ideas of Grimson and Demetri Terzopoulos.

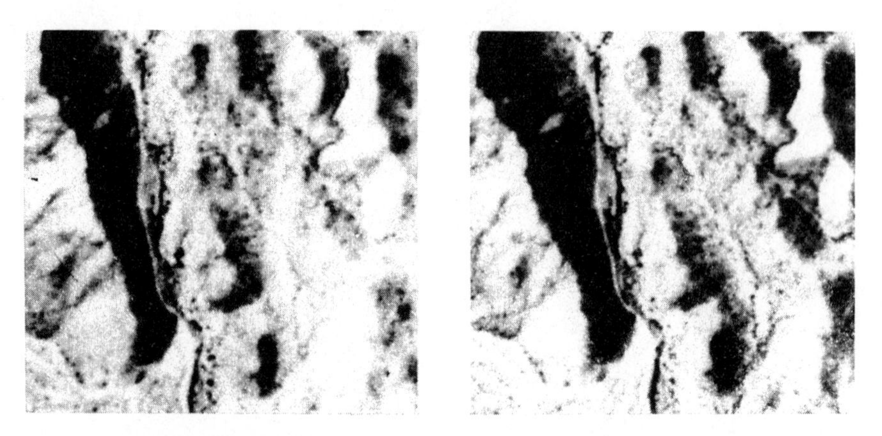

Figure 5 A stereo aerial image pair. The two pictures are arranged so that you can see depth yourself with the aid of a stereoscopic viewer. Courtesy of W. Eric L. Grimson.

Figure 6 A contour map produced from the aerial images in Figure 5. Courtesy of W. Eric L. Grimson.

Computers Can Help Manufacture Products

It is fortunate that computers will eventually do work that people dislike — jobs that are dirty, dangerous, demeaning, hopelessly boring, or poorly rewarded. As society advances, such jobs must be done by flexible, intelligent robots or by an armamentarium of special-purpose machines using brute-force methods. So far, the special-purpose machines dominate. Hardly anyone has shoes made to order, even though one person's two feet are rarely the same size. Tailor-made suits have similarly given way to the standard item off the rack.

To move from special-purpose machines to flexible, intelligent robots requires many capabilities. One of these is reasoning about motion in space. Faced with moving the small brick from one place to another in the cluttered environment shown in Figure 7, a spatial-reasoning program by Rodney A. Brooks and Tomás Lozano-Pérez decides that it can move the brick through the gap between the obstacles after rotation.

Another requirement is the capability of dealing with force and touch information. A program developed by W. Daniel Hillis can distinguish among screws, washers, cotter pins, and other small objects using information from touch sensors. The touch sensors can be carried by fingers like the tendon-actuated one, developed by Steve Jacobsen and John E. Wood, shown in Figure 8.

Computers Can Learn from Examples and Precedents

Several programs now demonstrate learning talent. One of my programs learns new concepts from sequences like the one shown in Figure 9 for learning about arches. Another, INDUCE, by Ryszard S. Michalski, learns to distinguish between the upper trains and the lower trains shown in Figure 10. In a practical application, the

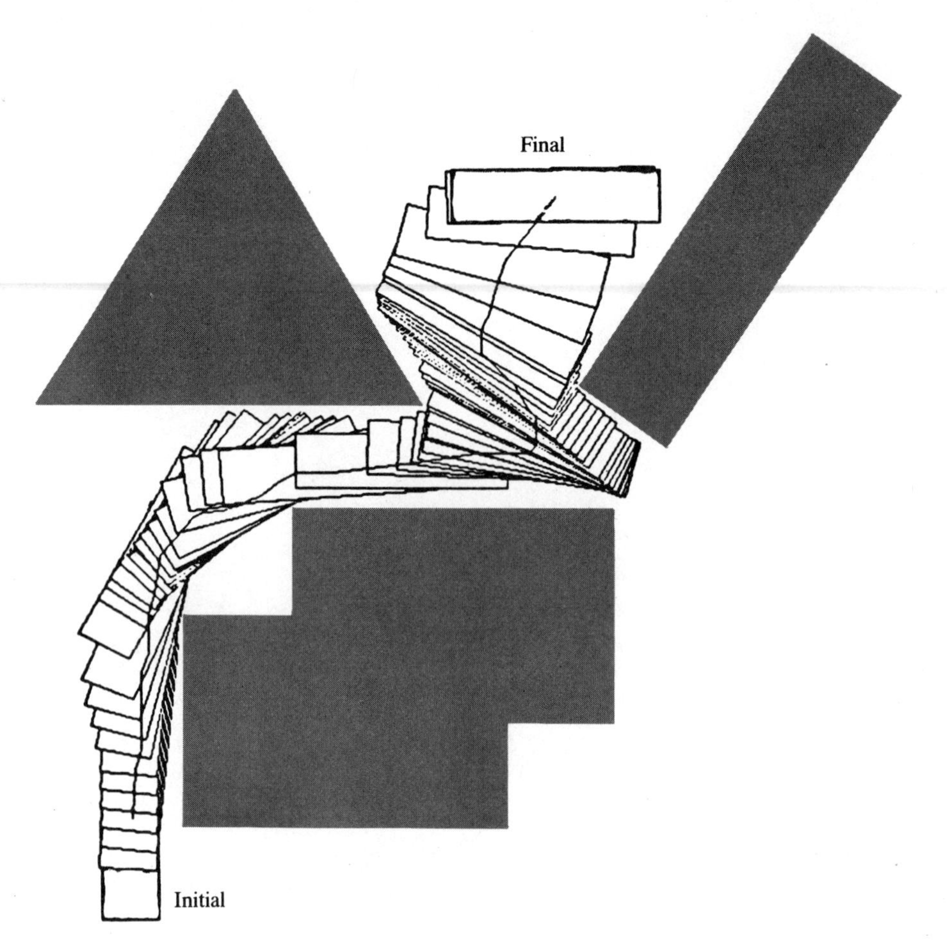

Figure 7 A simple spatial-reasoning problem. The solution is to rotate the brick as it is moved through the strait between the obstacles. Courtesy of Rodney A. Brooks and Tomás Lozano-Pérez.

Figure 8 A tendon-actuated finger. The construction of such fingers requires sophisticated materials. Courtesy of Steven Jacobsen and John E. Wood.

train-recognition program learned criteria for recognizing more than a dozen soybean diseases, producing results superior to human specialists. Since a considerable fraction of the world's population relies on soybeans for survival, accurate soybean-disease diagnosis is extremely important.

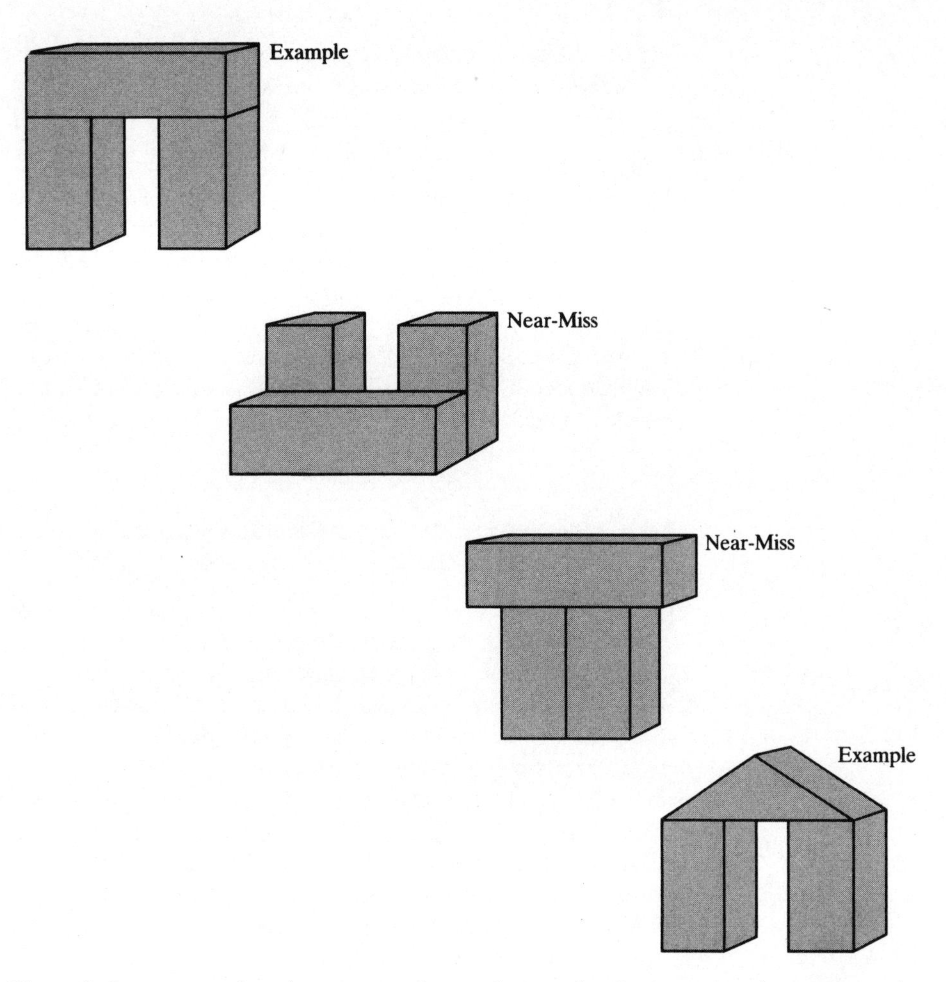

Figure 9 One concept-learning program learns about arches from a series of examples and near misses. The program decides that an arch is a brick or wedge that must be supported by two bricks that cannot touch.

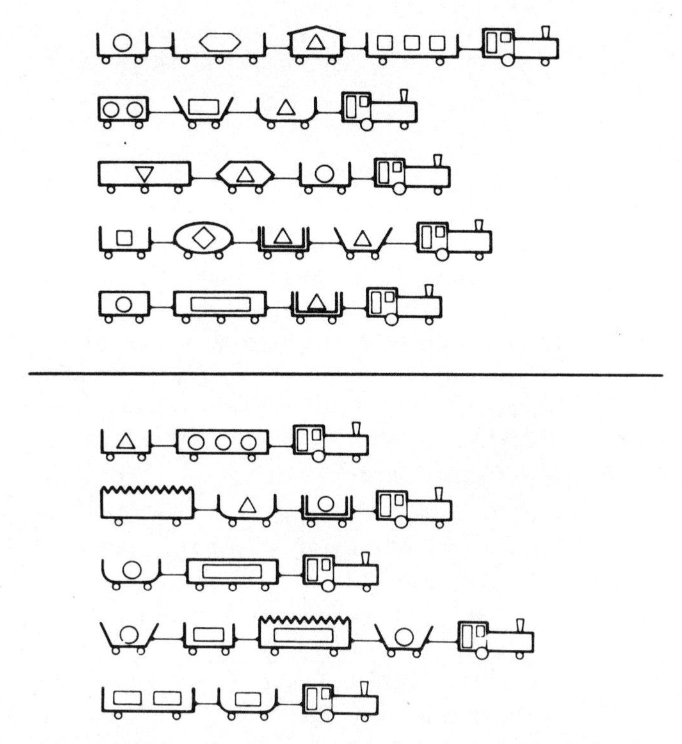

Figure 10 Another concept-learning program describes the upper trains as those having a short car with a closed top; it describes the lower ones as those having either two cars or a car with a jagged top. Courtesy of Ryszard S. Michalski.

Another kind of learning program, by me, deals with precedents and exercises like those captured by the following brief descriptions:

Macbeth

This is a story about Macbeth, Lady Macbeth, Duncan, and Macduff. Macbeth is an evil noble. Lady Macbeth is a greedy, ambitious woman. Duncan is a king. Macduff is a noble. Lady Macbeth persuades Macbeth to want to be king because she is greedy. She is able to influence him because he is married to her and because he is weak. Macbeth murders Duncan with a knife. Macbeth murders Duncan because Macbeth wants to be king and because Macbeth is evil. Lady Macbeth kills herself. Macduff is angry. Macduff kills Macbeth because Macbeth murdered Duncan and because Macduff is loyal to Duncan.

An Exercise

Let E be an exercise. E is a story about a weak noble and a greedy lady. The lady is married to the noble. Show that the noble may want to be king.

Told by a teacher that *Macbeth* is to be considered a precedent, the program forms a rule to the effect that the weakness of a nobleman and the greed of his wife can cause him to want to be king. The same program can learn what things look like from functional definitions, some background knowledge, and particular examples.

Still another learning program, by Douglas B. Lenat, one more oriented toward teacher-free discovery, deals with concepts like multiplication, factorization, and prime number. It demonstrates that a program can invent mathematics that even professional mathematicians find interesting and exciting. In particular, Lenat's mathematical discovery program stumbled across the obscure idea of maximally divisible numbers, even though the program's author, and evidently most other mathematicians, had never thought about maximally divisible numbers before. The distinguished mathematician Ramanujan had, however, so Lenat's program is in good company.

Computers Can Model Animal Information Processing

Many psychologists do Artificial Intelligence because they want to understand animal perception and cognition from an information-processing point of view. Programs join animals as test subjects, with behavior differences between programs and animals becoming as interesting as behavior itself. Part of the research focuses on vision, hearing, and touch, and part addresses human problem solving.

CRITERIA FOR SUCCESS

Any field must have criteria for determining if work has been successful. In some fields, the criteria are firmly established. Criteria for success in Artificial Intelligence are not so firmly established because the field is still young, it is extremely broad, and much of it does not seem susceptible to conventional mathematical treatment.

Still, we need some working criteria for judging results, even if the criteria prove transient. Consequently, let us demand good answers to these questions before we take some particular work in Artificial Intelligence to be successful:

- Is the task clearly defined?
- Is there an implemented procedure performing the defined task? If not, much difficulty may be lying under a rug somewhere.
- Is there a set of identifiable regularities or constraints from which the implemented procedure gets its power? If not, the procedure may be an ad hoc toy, capable perhaps of superficially impressive performance on carefully selected examples, but incapable of deeply impressive performance and incapable of revealing any principles.

All of the examples cited in this chapter satisfy these criteria: all perform clearly defined tasks; all involve implemented procedures; and all involve identified regularities or constraints.

SUMMARY

- Artificial Intelligence has tremendous applications in many socially relevant areas. Leaders in a wide variety of fields need to know its ideas.
- As a means for studying intelligence, working with computers and with computer-based metaphors offers certain clear advantages. Results are more likely to be precise, to provide bounds on the amount of information processing required, and to be testable experimentally.
- Intelligent behavior can be displayed along several dimensions. This is made possible by strength in information-processing capability associated with certain basic areas. These areas include matching, goal reduction, constraint exploitation, search, control, problem solving, and logic.
- Finally, computers already can do many things that seem to require intelligence.

From *Computer Aided Design*, November 1985, by J. Gero (ed.)

EDITORIAL

Expert systems in CAD

Computers and computing are slowly becoming an integral part of design, they are already indispensible in analysis. Computers are being used in office and job management functions. They are being used increasingly to produce drawings and other graphical representations to communicate ideas. There are also some in use as design aids in a small number of offices. All of these applications are built on two fundamental concepts. The first concept is that the world of interest can be described by the 'calculus of real numbers – algebra'. The second concept has to do with computing itself and is concerned with the way we make computers work, through instructions to the computer codified as 'procedures', which describe what must be done. These we call computer programs; a set of detailed instructions which are executed sequentially, unless the program contains instructions which alter this sequential flow. Whilst this is a concept deeply embedded in traditional computing it has important ramifications for users. Such computing is called von Neumann computing after the inventor of this architecture for computing.

Design is concerned with concepts, ideas, judgment and experience. All of these appear to be outside the realm of traditional computing. Human beings discourse with each other using models of their worlds largely unrelated to either mathematical descriptions or procedural representations. They make use of knowledge about objects, events and processes and make declarative statements about them. These are often written down symbolically. The limits of traditional computing are that is is unable to represent and manipulate knowledge in an explicit and coherent form and that it is unable to perform symbolic computation.

KNOWLEDGE ENGINEERING

Knowledge engineering is a subfield of artificial intelligence. It is concerned with the acquisition, representation and manipulation of human knowledge in symbolic form. Human knowledge is thought of as being reasoning (rather than the simple ability to acquire facts as you might find in an encyclopedia). Just as the industrial revolution can be considered to have automated mechanical power, and the computer revolution to have automated calculation, so knowledge engineering automates reasoning.

Feigenbaum (E A Feigenbaum 'The art of artificial intelligence: themes and case studies in knowledge engineering' *IJCAI-77* William Kaufmann, Los Altos (1977) pp 1014–1029) defines the activity of knowledge engineering as follows:

> The knowledge engineer practices the art of bringing the principles and tools of artificial intelligence research to bear on difficult application problems requiring experts' knowledge for their solution. The technical issues of acquiring this knowledge, representing it, and using it appropriately to construct and explain lines of reasoning are important in the design of knowledge-based systems . . . The art of constructing intelligent agents is both part of and an extension of the programming art. It is the art of building complex computer programs that represent and reason with knowledge of the world.

The fundamental structure used to represent reasoning and, hence, knowledge, is symbolic inference. Inference is based on well established logic principles and has been extended to operate on symbols. The obvious advantage of inferencing is that it does not require an *a priori* mathematical theory such as is found in, say, hydraulics or structures. It can be used to manipulate concepts. Barr and Feigenbaum (A Barr and E Feigenbaum (eds) *Handbook of artificial intelligence* Vol 1, William Kaufmann, Los Altos (1981)), talking about the applicability of knowledge engineering in conceptual areas, state:

> Since there are no mathematical cores to structure the calculational use of the computer, such areas will inevitably be served by symbolic models and symbolic inference techniques.

EXPERT SYSTEMS

Expert systems have been defined as intelligent computer programs which use symbolic inference procedures to deal with problems that are difficult enough to require significant human expertise for their solution.

Human experts can be compared with conventional computer programs (see J Lansdown: 'Expert systems: their impact on the construction industry' *RIBA Conf.* Fund, London (1982)):

- Human skills arise from the possession of expert ability and knowledge in a specific subject area. These skills grow as more and more experience is gained.
- Human experts can explain and, if necessary, defend the advice they give and are aware of its wider implications.
- Human experts determine which knowledge is applicable rather than proceeding algorithmically – step by step.
- Human experts can, and frequently have to, act with partial information. In order to supplement this, they ask only sufficient and pertinent questions to allow them to arrive at a conclusion.

Conventional computer programs differ markedly from programs which act as experts, specifically:

- They are usually complex and difficult for anyone other than their designers to understand.
- They embody their knowledge of the subject area in terms designed for computational efficiency such that this knowledge is intertwined with the control parts of the program. Thus, the knowledge is implicit in the program in such a way which makes it difficult to alter or change.
- They cannot suggest to their users why they need a particular fact nor justify their results.

Thus, expert systems aim to capture the ability of human experts to ask pertinent questions, to explain why they are asking them, and to defend their conclusions. These aspects are unrelated to a specific domain of knowledge and apply to all experts.

Expert systems are computer programs which attempt to behave in a manner similar to rational human experts. They all share a common fundamental architecture even if the knowledge encoding mechanisms differ. An expert system will have the following components:

- an inference engine
  - this carries out the reasoning tasks and makes the system act like an expert
- a knowledge base
  - this contains the expert's domain specific knowledge and is quite separate from the inference engine
- an explanation facility
  - this interacts with both the knowledge base and the inference engine to explain why an answer is needed at a particular point or how a question can be answered; further it is used to explain how a conclusion was reached or to explain why a specific conclusion could not be reached
- a state description
  - this contains the facts which have been inferred to be true and those which have been found to be false during a particular session
- a natural language interface
  - few expert systems have this yet

KNOWLEDGE AS INFERENCE

There are a variety of possible ways of encoding knowledge. These include state-space representations, logic-based representations, procedural representations, semantic nets, production systems and frame systems. Although many of these approaches may be mapped on to each other the one we shall concern ourselves with here is the one which allows us to directly encode knowledge as inference – namely logic based representations.

Logic-based representations make use of a special subset of logic called predicate calculus and within that subset another subset concerned with first order predicate calculus.

Predicate calculus allows us to write single inferences dependent on many conditions of the form:

A is true if
    B is true
and *C* is true
or *D* is true

('true' does not mean truth in the veracity sense, rather in terms of the relationship of *A* to *B*, *C* and *D*).

We could infer that *A* is true from the above inference statement if *B* and *C* or *D* are true – we call such an inference statement knowledge, to distinguish it from a fact which is the outcome of the inference process.

We could write down some structural knowledge as:

X is a rigid frame if
    X is composed of linear members
and actions in *X* are transferred at joints by bending

Thus, we would be in the position to 'know' whether any *X* was a rigid frame based on the truth of the two statements following the 'if'.

More formally, such inference statements are called predicates. The statement before the 'if' is called the head of the predicate while the statements following the 'if' are called the body of the predicate. Thus, a predicate with both a head and a body is knowledge while a predicate with a head only, is a fact by our earlier definition.

It is convenient at this stage to reexamine the idea of databases. Databases in this context are used to store representations of designs and their performance. For example, we store the results of an analysis in a database possibly to be used by a graphics program. Similarly, we can store the facts we have inferred or directly placed into the system in a facts base and the knowledge in a knowledge base. Such bases are different to databases in a number of important aspects.

Facts and knowledge bases can be added to, and subtracted from, without affecting the integrity of the remainder of the base. The knowledge base is the computer program and we can have inconsistent facts and other programs for the knowledge to work with. Knowledge can become facts after suitable inferencing.

We can place facts explicitly into the system as a predicate without a body, such as '*X* is a rigid frame'. We can place knowledge into the system using predicates with bodies. This knowledge is both symbolic and manipulable (it can, of course, include normal arithmetic and algebraic operations). By allowing the knowledge to operate on available facts we can get the system to carry out the inferencing process to infer whether the head of a predicate is true. If it is, it becomes an inferred fact and can be stored in the facts base.

Thus, we can store both knowledge explicitly (as inferences) and facts. The designer can evaluate the knowledge for correctness, ie does it represent what he wants it to represent. More likely, the designer uses the system to infer new facts and uses his professional judgment to evaluate these facts in order to extract the architectural or engineering meaning from them.

PROBLEM-SOLVING PARADIGMS

Much of Artificial Intelligence is about problem solving. Consequently, competence in Artificial Intelligence requires access to an armamentarium of problem-solving paradigms. [...]

In this chapter, we concentrate on two..., particularly popular problem-solving paradigms, *generate-and-test systems* and *rule-based systems.* We work with generate-and-test systems first. Variations on the generate-and-test problem-solving paradigm appear in a wide variety of practical systems: one system finds airplanes in airport pictures using a kind of controlled hallucination; another identifies organic-chemical structures from their mass spectrograms.

Second, we study *rule-based systems,* also known as *production systems.* The rule-based-system paradigm is the one that is most popular in *knowledge engineering*, the part of Artificial Intelligence specialized for building *expert systems.* Some rule-based expert systems do *synthesis.* XCON configures computers, for example. Other rule-based expert systems do *analysis.* MYCIN diagnoses infectious diseases, and PROSPECTOR interprets oil-well logs. Both synthesis- and analysis-oriented rule-based systems can explain how and why they do things, and they can estimate the quality of their results.

[...]

In studying this chapter, you learn that the problem-solving paradigms explained are strong enough to make important, economically exciting problem solvers. On the other side, you must realize that these paradigms, by themselves, are too weak to support many of the characteristics of human experts (hence we will avoid the common designation *expert system*).

GENERATE AND TEST

Problem solvers adhering to the *generate-and-test paradigm* use two basic modules. One module, the *generator*, enumerates possible solutions. The second, the *tester*, evaluates each proposed solution, either accepting it or rejecting it.

Depending on the purpose and the nature of the problem, the generator may generate all possible solutions before the tester takes over, or alternatively, generation and testing may be interdigitated. Action may stop when one acceptable solution is found, or action may continue until some satisfactory number of solutions is found, or action may continue until all possible solutions are generated and tested.

Generate-and-test Systems Often Do Identification

The generate-and-test paradigm is used most frequently to solve identification problems involving no more than a few hundred possible answers. In identification problems, the generator is said to produce hypotheses.

To use the generate-and-test paradigm to identify, say, a tree, you can reach for a tree book, thumb through it page by page, stopping when you find a picture that looks like the tree to be identified. Thumbing through the book is the generation procedure; matching the pictures to the tree is the testing procedure.

To use generate and test to burgle a three-number, two-digit safe, you can start with the combination 00-00-00, move to 00-00-01, and continue on through all possible combinations until the door opens. Of course, the counting is the generation procedure, and the twist of the safe handle is the testing procedure.

The burglar in Figure 1 may take some time with this approach, however, for there are $100^3 = 1$ million combinations. At three a minute, figuring he will have to go through half on the average, to succeed, the job will take about 16 weeks, if he works 24 hours a day.

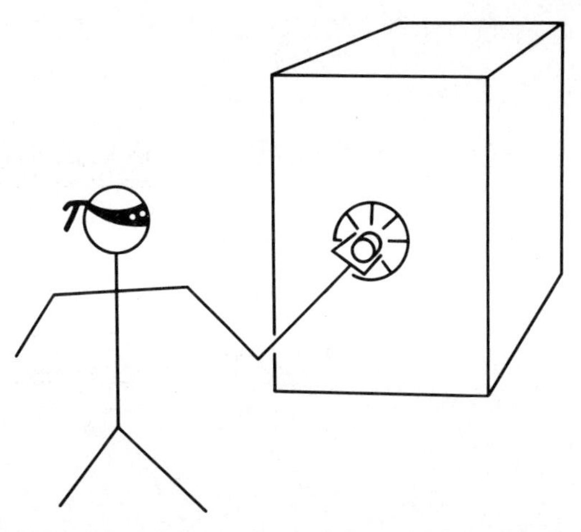

Figure 1 An example illustrating the generate-and-test paradigm. The generator is the procedure the safecracker uses to select and dial combinations. The tester is the burglar working with the handle. Careful safecrackers make sure they try all possibilities, without any repeats, until the handle works.

Generators Should Be Complete, Nonredundant, and Informed

It is obvious that good generators have three properties:

- Good generators are complete. They eventually produce all possible solutions.
- Good generators are nonredundant. They never damage efficiency by proposing the same solution twice.
- Good generators are informed. They use possibility-limiting information, restricting the solutions they propose accordingly.

Informability is important because there are often too many solutions to go through otherwise. Consider the tree-identification example. If it is winter and a tree we are trying to identify is bare, we do not bother going through a tree book's conifer section.

Similarly, if a burglar knows, somehow, that all of the numbers in a safe combination are prime numbers in the range from 0 to 99, then he can confine himself to $25^3 = 15\,625$ numbers, getting the safe open in less than 2 days, on the average, instead of 16 weeks.

Analyzing Mass Spectrograms Illustrates Generate-and-test

Suppose an organic chemist wants to know the chemical nature of something newly created in the test tube. The first step, not the one of concern here, is to determine the number of atoms of various kinds in one molecule of the stuff. This is given by a chemical formula, such as $C_8H_{16}O$, which is the example used throughout this discussion. The notation indicates that each molecule has eight atoms of carbon, sixteen of hydrogen, and one of oxygen.

Once a sample's chemical formula is known, the chemist uses the sample's mass spectrogram to work out the way the atoms are arranged in the chemical's structure, thus identifying the isomer of the chemical that constitutes the sample.

The mass spectrogram is produced as indicated in Figure 2. The spectrogram machine bombards a sample with high-energy electrons, causing the molecules to break up into charged chunks of various sizes. Then the chunks are sorted by sending them through a magnetic field that deflects the high-charge, low-weight ones more than the low-charge, high-weight ones. The deflected chunks are collected, forming the spectrogram.

Figure 3*a* shows a typical spectrogram. The purpose of the DENDRAL system is to work, like a knowledgeable chemist, from a chemical formula and spectrogram to a deduced structure. Such a chemical formula and deduced chemical structure are shown in Figure 3*b*.

As indicated in Figure 4, the DENDRAL system works out structures from chemical formulas and mass spectrograms using generate and test:

- The chemical formula is fed to a structure enumerator capable of generating all possible structures. The structure enumerator limits its output to things consistent with the given chemical formula.

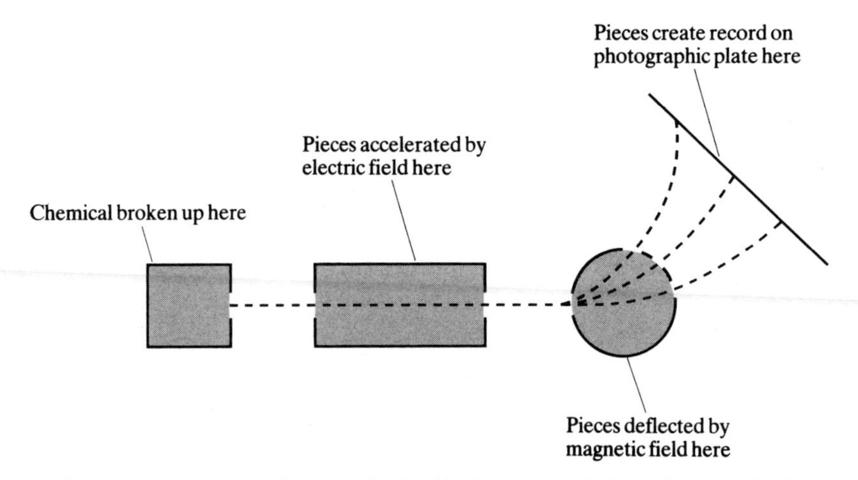

Figure 2 A mass spectrometer. An organic chemical under study is broken up, the fragments are separated according to their mass-to-charge ratio, and the results are recorded, making a mass spectrogram.

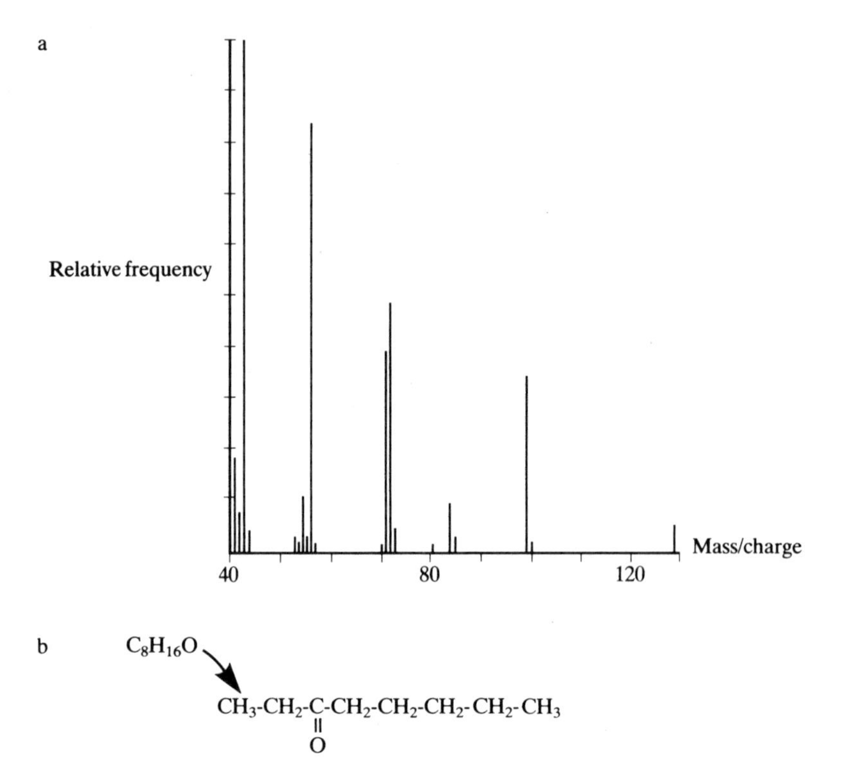

Figure 3 Part *a* shows a mass spectrogram. Organic chemists use such mass spectrograms, together with chemical formulas to deduce chemical structures. Part *b* shows a chemical formula and a structure consistent with the formula, with general knowledge of chemical structure, and with the given mass spectrogram. Adapted from *Machine Intelligence 4*, copyright 1969 by American Elsevier Publishing Company, New York.

- The structure enumerator receives information to the effect that certain substructures must be present and others must not be present. The substructure lists come primarily from a preliminary analysis of the spectrogram. (This preliminary analysis is described in a later section.)
- A mass spectrogram is synthesized for each structure generated. The combination of the structure enumerator and the mass-spectrogram synthesizer constitutes the generator required by the generate-and-test paradigm. It is complete and nonredundant because it uses a provably complete and nonredundant structure-enumeration procedure. It is informed because the structure-enumeration procedure uses the chemical formula and knowledge about necessary and forbidden substructures.

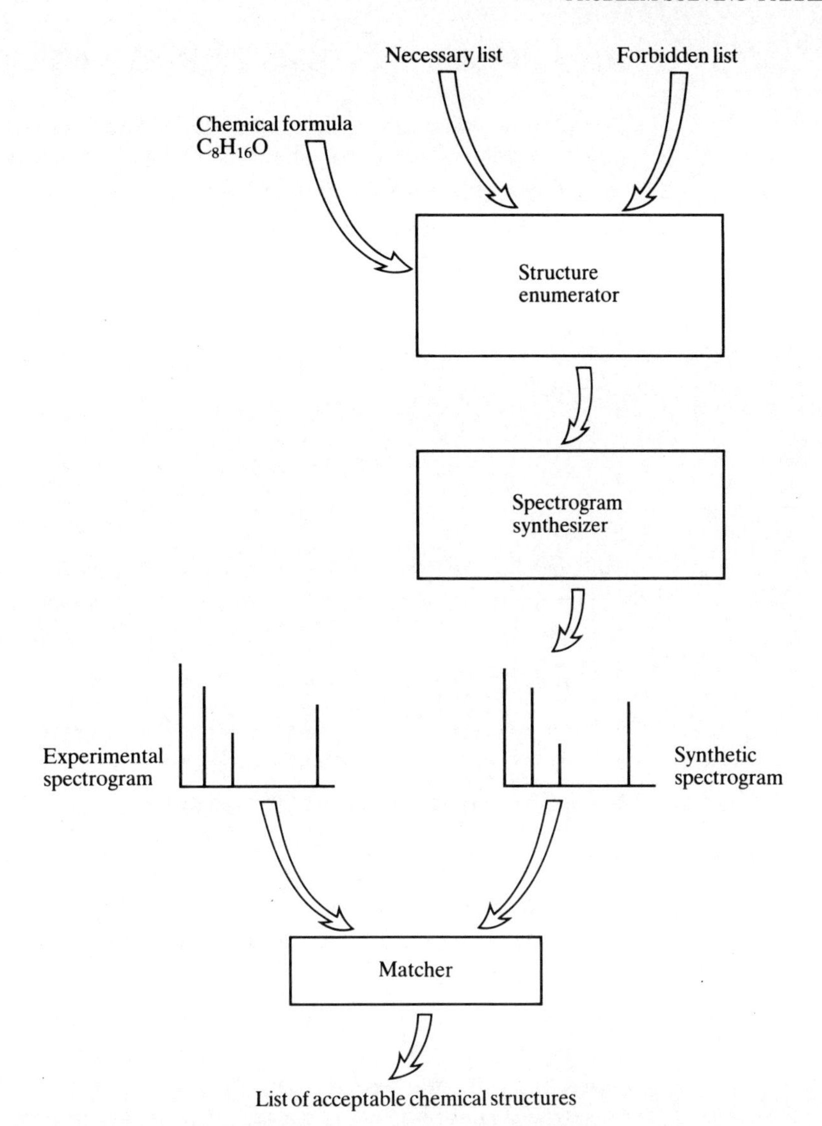

Figure 4 DENDRAL uses the generate-and-test paradigm to find chemical structures. The structure enumerator is influenced by lists of necessary and forbidden fragments. A spectrogram synthesizer produces a synthetic spectrogram for each proposed chemical structure. The enumeration of possible structures is complete, nonredundant, and informed. A proposed chemical structure is accepted if its synthetic spectrogram yields a good match with the experimental spectrogram.

- The synthetic mass spectrograms are all compared with the real experimental spectrogram. The possible structures are those whose synthetic spectrograms match the real one adequately. The structure judged correct is the one whose synthetic spectrogram matches the real one best. The matcher constitutes the tester of the generate-and-test paradigm.

The matcher could work by forming a sum of the squares of the differences in spectrogram-peak heights, the sort of standard engineering measure of signal difference. The actual DENDRAL matcher is more involved because it is necessary to recognize that some peaks are more significant than others. The procedure used does this by way of the following:

- Certain break-up rules mark their products as especially significant.
- If any so-marked significant peak is not in the experimental spectrogram, then the structure that predicted that significant peak is rejected outright.
- The remaining spectrograms are then ranked according to how many of the experimental peaks each accounts for. The remaining spectrograms rarely tie.

This matcher usually eliminates all but a few structures, which then are reported in the order of their likelihood. In the $C_8H_{16}O$ example, with the given spectrogram, only one structure survives.

[...]

RULE-BASED SYSTEMS FOR SYNTHESIS

So far, most successful synthesis systems and analysis systems embody the rule-based problem-solving paradigm. Rule-based problem-solving systems are built around rules like the following one, which consists of an *if* part and a *then* part:

R*n* If condition 1
condition 2
.
.
.
then action 1
action 2
.
.
.

To work forward with such rules, moving from condition-specifying *if* parts to action-specifying *then* parts, we use *forward-chaining*, and we speak of a *forward-chaining condition-action system* containing *condition-action rules.*

Here is the procedure for forward chaining:

To forward-chain using if-then rules:

1 Until a problem is solved or no rule's *if* parts are satisfied by the current situation:
  1.1 Collect rules whose *if* parts are satisfied. If more than one rule's *if* parts are satisfied, use a conflict-resolution strategy to eliminate all but one.
  1.2 Do what the rule's *then* parts say to do.

When all the conditions in a rule are satisfied by the current situation, the rule is said to be *triggered.* When the actions are performed, the rule is said to be *fired.* Triggering does not always mean firing, because the conditions of several rules may be satisfied simultaneously, triggering them all, making it necessary for a conflict-resolution procedure to decide which rule actually fires. Several conflict-resolution procedures will be discussed presently, while some examples are developed.

The first example involves a synthesis-oriented, forward-chaining, rule-based toy system for bagging groceries. The next example involves a practical system for laying out computer systems. The layout system, XCON, is one of the harbingers of Artificial Intelligence's penetration into engineering design.

A Toy Synthesis System Bags Groceries

Suppose we want Robbie, our robot, to bag groceries in the manner of a grocery-store checkout clerk. We are not interested in optimal packing, but we do want Robbie to know some of the fundamentals of grocery bagging: big bottles of Pepsi go in the bottom, with not too many in any one bag; ice cream is protected with freezer bags; and little things are stuffed here and there when everything else is in place.

We will have Robbie approach the job using BAGGER, a rule-based synthesis system. BAGGER involves four steps, as shown by the following procedure description:

BAGGER:

1 Check what the customer has selected, looking over the groceries to see if something may be missing, with a view toward suggesting additions to the customer.
2 Bag the large items, with special attention to putting big bottles in first.
3 Bag the medium items, taking care to put frozen things in freezer bags.
4 Bag the small items, putting them wherever there is room.

And, of course, whenever necessary, BAGGER commands Robbie to start a fresh bag.

Now let us see how this knowledge can be captured in if-then rules. First, we need a database for the rules to look at. The database certainly must contain information about the items in each bag, the items yet to be bagged, and the current step. Here is a suitable database for illustrating what is involved:

Step: Check-order
Bag1:
Unbagged: Bread
Glop
Granola (2)
Ice cream
Potato chips

In addition, the rules need access to information about the size and other properties of various items:

Item	*Container Type*	*Size*	*Frozen?*
Bread	Plastic bag	Medium	No
Glop	Jar	Small	No
Granola	Cardboard box	Large	No
Ice cream	Cardboard carton	Medium	Yes
Pepsi	Bottle	Large	No
Potato chips	Plastic bag	Medium	No

Note that the database contains a step name. Each of the rules in BAGGER's rule base tests the step name. The effect is a partitioning of the rules into packets suited to each bagging step. For example, activation of the following rule is limited to the check-order step by a check-order condition:

B1 If the step is check-order
there is a bag of potato chips
there is no soft-drink bottle

then add one bottle of Pepsi to the order

The purpose of the rule is to be sure the customer has something to drink to go along with potato chips, since potato chips are dry and salty.

Since we are interested only in illustrating some points, not in capturing all of bagging knowledge, let us move on immediately to a rule to get us out of order checking and into the next step. The following rule does this, getting us into the bag-large-items step:

B2 If the step is check-order
then discontinue the check-order step
start the bag-large-items step

At first, this rule may seem dangerous, for it looks as though it could trigger at any time the check-order step, preventing the other rule from doing its legitimate and necessary work. No problem; we simply adopt a suitable conflict-resolution strategy. Here are some possibilities:

- *Specificity ordering.* Suppose the conditions of one triggering rule are a superset of the conditions of another triggering rule. Use the rule with the superset on the ground that it is more specialized to the current situation.
- *Rule ordering.* Arrange all rules in one long priority list. The triggering rule appearing earliest in the list has the highest priority. The others are ignored.
- *Data ordering.* Arrange all possible aspects of the situation in one long priority list. The triggering rule having the highest priority condition has the highest priority.
- *Size ordering.* Assign the highest priority to the triggering rule with the toughest requirements, where toughest means the longest list of constraining conditions.
- *Recency ordering.* Consider the most recently used rule to have the highest priority, or consider the least recent to have the highest priority, at the designer's whim.

- *Context limiting.* Reduce the likelihood of conflict by separating the rules into groups, only some of which are active at any time. Have a procedure that activates and deactivates groups.

Of course, having a set of possibilities to choose among does not mean we have a science of conflict resolution. Selection of a strategy is done ad hoc, for the most part.

Note that BAGGER uses the context-limiting strategy because, by convention, the first condition clause of each rule limits the rule to a particular step.

Assume BAGGER also uses the specificity-ordering conflict-resolution strategy. This means that the B2 check-order rule never can fire as long as any other check-order rule triggers. Each step has a rule just like B2 to switch into the next step when nothing else can be done.

Using specificity-ordering conflict resolution helps out in other ways as well. Consider, for example the first two rules for bagging large items:

B3 If the step is bag-large-items
there is a large item to be bagged
there is a large bottle to be bagged
there is a bag with <6 large items
then put the bottle in the bag

B4 If the step is bag-large-items
there is a large item to be bagged
there is a bag with <6 large items
then put the large item in the bag

Big items go into bags that do not have too many items already, but the bottles, being heavy, go in first. The extra condition in B3 ensures this ordering. When there is a large bottle, both rules' conditions will match, but B3's conditions are a superset of B4's, so B3 takes precedence.

Of course, we need a way of handling large bottles and other large items if there is no room in any bag. This is done by B5:

B5 If the step is bag-large-items
there is a large item to be bagged
then start a fresh bag

And finally, another step-changing rule moves us on to the next step:

B6 If the step is bag-large-items
then discontinue the bag-large-items step
start the bag-medium-items step

With the database given, simulating the rules given so far, we have one bag containing Pepsi and granola, as shown here:

Step: Bag-medium-items
Bag1: Pepsi
Granola (2)

Unbagged: Bread
Glop
Ice cream
Potato chips

Now it is time to look at some rules for bagging medium items:

B7 If the step is bag-medium-items
there is a medium item to be bagged
there is an empty bag or a bag with medium items
the bag is not yet full
the medium item is frozen
the medium item is not in an insulated freezer bag
then put the medium item in an insulated freezer bag

B8 If the step is bag-medium-items
there is a medium item to be bagged
there is an empty bag or a bag with medium items
the bag is not yet full
then put the medium item in the bag

Again, the specificity-ordering conflict-resolution strategy works. If both B7 and B8 are matched, B7 wins, ensuring that frozen things are placed in insulated freezer bags before bagging.

The bag-medium-items step also needs these rules, one to get new bags going and one to get into the next and final step:

B9	If	the step is bag-medium-items
		there is a medium item to be bagged
	then	start a fresh bag
B10	If	the step is bag-medium-items
	then	discontinue the bag-medium-items step
		start the bag-small-items step

At this point, after execution of all appropriate bag-medium-item rules, we have the following database:

Step:	Bag-small-items
Bag1:	Pepsi
	Granola (2)
Bag2:	Bread
	Ice cream (in freezer bag)
	Potato chips
Unbagged:	Glop

Note that, according to the rules, medium items do not go into bags with large items. This is not true for small items, for the next rules can put them anywhere, but not in a bottle-holding bag, if others are available:

B11	If	the step is bag-small-items
		there is a small item
		there is a bag that is not yet full
		the bag does not contain bottles
	then	put the small item in the bag
B12	If	the step is bag-small-items
		there is a small item
		there is a bag that is not yet full
	then	put the small item in the bag

We still need a rule to get a new bag:

B13	If	the step is bag-small-items
		there is a small item
	then	start a fresh bag

And we need a rule to terminate action when done:

B14	If	the step is bag-small-items
	then	discontinue the bag-small-items step
		stop

Here is the final result for our illustration, after all rules have been used:

Step:	Stop
Bag1:	Pepsi
	Granola (2)
Bag2:	Bread
	Ice cream (in freezer bag)
	Potato chips
	Glop
Unbagged:	

XCON Configures Computer Systems

Now it is time to consider an example of a real rule-based synthesis system resembling BAGGER. The XCON system is appropriate, for it is famous, yet simple. Like BAGGER, XCON is a forward-chaining system.

XCON's domain concerns computer-system components. When a company buys a big computer, it buys a central processor, memory, terminals, disk drives, tape drives, various peripheral controllers, and other paraphernalia. All this must be arranged sensibly along input/output busses. Moreover, all the electronic modules must be placed in the proper kind of cabinet in a suitable slot of a suitable backplane.

Getting things arranged and placed is a task called *configuration.* Doing configuration is tedious because a typical computer component family has hundreds of possible options that can come together in an unthinkable number of combinations.

Like BAGGER, XCON does its job in stages:

XCON:

1 Check the order, looking for mismatched items and missing components.
2 Lay out the processor in cabinets.
3 Put boxes in the input/output cabinets, and put components in those boxes.
4 Put panels in the input/output cabinets.
5 Lay out the floor plan.
6 Do the cabling.

To handle these steps. XCON uses rules like this representative pair:

X1 If the context is layout and assigning a power supply
an sbi module of any type has been put in a cabinet
the position it occupies in the cabinet is known
there is space available in the cabinet for a power supply
there is no available power supply
the voltage and frequency of the components is known
then add an appropriate power supply

X2 If the context is layout and assigning a power supply
an sbi module of any type has been put in a cabinet
the position it occupies in the cabinet is known
there is space available in the cabinet for a power supply
there is an available power supply
then put the power supply in the cabinet in the available space

The first rule acts rather like the one in BAGGER that adds Pepsi if the order contains potato chips but no beverage. The second is a typical insertion rule. The context mentioned in both rules is a combination of the top-level step and a substep.

Like BAGGER, XCON uses the context-limiting and the specificity-ordering conflict-resolution strategies. Context limiting is done by making the first clause in each rule conditional on what is going on. Specificity ordering enables XCON to use rules like the following one for switching contexts:

X3 If the current context is x
then deactivate the x context
activate the y context

This has the effect of deleting one item from the context designation and adding another. It fires only if no other rule associated with the context triggers, for any other triggering rule would have conditions that are a superset of unaccompanied context checking.

Curiously, XCON hardly ever backs up. For the most part, it forges ahead like BAGGER. Evidently, the domain is such that the rules embody enough constraint to prevent going into blind alleys, generally.

At the moment, XCON is a 2500-rule system and growing. XCON knows the properties of several hundred component types for VAX computers, made by Digital Equipment Corporation. XCON routinely handles orders involving one- or two-hundred components. It is representative of many similar systems for marketing and manufacturing.

Soon people will forget how to configure well, but that does not matter: people wanting to learn can study a rule-based configuration system. XCON, after all, demonstrates that a rule-based system can embody all the configuration knowledge needed to do configuration well.

From *Computer Aided Design* journal, April 1989

AI-based design versus geometry-based design or Why design cannot be supported by geometry alone

T Smithers

The reasons why the methodology and techniques underlying CAD systems cannot be used as the basis for engineering design support systems required to integrate computer-based support of the engineering design process are given. An argument is put forward that a combination of artificial intelligence techniques and geometric modelling techniques can meet these requirements.

geometric modelling, artificial intelligence, design support systems

This paper sets out to explain why the methodology and techniques underlying today's computer-aided drafting or design (CAD) systems cannot be used as the basis for the more powerful engineering design support systems required to more closely integrate computer-based support of the engineering design process. It also argues that a tightly integrated combination of artificial intelligence (AI) techniques, together with geometric modelling techniques, can meet these more demanding requirements.

In the next section, the development of the techniques which are most commonly used in today's CAD systems is reviewed, and some survey papers pointing to the considerable body of literature are referenced. There follows a brief review of the ideas and techniques developed under the label 'AI-based design'. This review includes explicit references to a wide selection of the AI-based design literature, since good survey papers on the subject have yet to be written. Having reviewed both geometry-based design and AI-based design, an activity-based model of the engineering design process is described. This model is presented as a framework for discussing the ability of geometry-based design and AI-based design techniques to support the engineering design process. Finally, some concluding remarks are made concerning the future of both geometry-based design and AI-based design systems and the methodologies that each is designed to support.

Department of Artificial Intelligence, University of Edinburgh, 5 Forrest Hill, Edinburgh EH1 2QL, UK

GEOMETRY-BASED DESIGN: A BRIEF REVIEW

Geometry-based design support systems, now more widely known as computer-aided drafting or design (CAD) systems, first became viable in the mid-1960s with the advent of sufficiently powerful computers and graphical display devices. These early systems were basically 2D drawing systems which provided a set of primitives (points, lines, circles, and perhaps arcs) from which engineering drawings could be constructed. In the early 1970s, systems were developed which could support limited 3D constructions in terms of points, lines, and arcs. These became known as wireframe models, for obvious reasons. At about the same time, parametric curved surface representation techniques were also being developed. Through the 1970s, *face* modelling systems became available which could support hidden-line and hidden-face removal, and thus the generation of more realistic pictures. This desire for ever more realistic pictures has since become one of the strongest themes of computer-based geometry modelling systems; wrongly so, in the opinion of the author, since important geometric modelling issues have been ignored as a result. During the late 1970s and early 1980s, two outstanding geometry modelling problems began to be solved: the modelling of free-form surfaces, or sculptured surfaces; and the modelling of solid objects, although the mathematical techniques used had been available for some time. These techniques are now implemented in a variety of geometry modelling systems currently available, although the modelling of sculptured surfaces and solid models has yet to be satisfactorily integrated in a general way.

The research and development of these geometric techniques is reported in a very extensive set of journal papers, reports, books, etc. Rather than attempt to point to these specifically, the following survey papers and books are referenced as ways into the literature. See Sutherland *et al.*[1], Rogers and Adams[2], Braid[3], Baer[4], Faux and Pratt[5], Requicha[6], Requicha and Voelcker[7], Foley and Van Dam[8], and Willis[9]. An excellent survey of all these techniques is presented in Woodwark[10].

Current free-form surface modelling techniques are mostly based upon surface patch techniques, B-splines, Bézier splines, and other parametric surface descriptions. These provide ways of representing complex curved surfaces from which it is reasonably easy to compute local characteristics of the surfaces being modelled; for displaying shaded images, for example. They are not, however, generally amenable to computations which require knowledge of more global aspects of the objects being modelled. A similar situation exists for the two most widely used solid modelling techniques; boundary representations, and set-theoretic techniques (sometimes referred to as constructive solid geometry – CSG). These two complementary techniques are good for representing the details of a particular solid object, but are not good for representing higher level aspects of it, such as the relationship between machined features, or the way in which features of one object are related to features of another object in an assembly. Indeed, the whole issue of 'features' in geometric modelling is still a vexed one.

The range of types of geometric shape that can be represented using the geometric modelling techniques available today, their *coverage*, is arguably not very good; there are important types of manufactured shapes that either cannot be represented easily, or cannot be represented at all. The failure to integrate free-form surface modelling and solid modelling techniques in a general way is responsible for a large part of this lack of coverage. The input languages to existing geometric modelling systems are also not well matched to the design process. Geometric design typically involves recognizing and establishing constraints, and the prescribing of values, yet modelling systems invariably require the user to prescribe fully defined constructions from a set of available primitives and operators.

Despite these limitations, the geometric techniques reviewed above have formed the basis of some powerful design aids developed over about the last twenty years. These systems, many of which are now commercially available, have become an established part of many engineering design offices, serving to aid some of the activities which make up the engineering design process. In any engineering design task, a number of diverse and conflicting requirements and constraints need to be resolved. In mechanical engineering, this resolution is typically expressed in terms of geometric shape. For example, in the design of a battery-operated torch, its weight, light-emitting capacity, and effective duration are all important, but competing, functional aspects. The resolution of these design requirements will be expressed in its overall geometric shape. The shape does not dictate the relationship between these functional aspects. Mechanical engineering design is thus geometrically dominated, and much of the knowledge generated and many of the ideas developed are presented and recorded in graphical or geometric forms, since this is a good way of expressing constraint resolutions. As a result, the impression has been created that geometry-based systems provide support for the full engineering design process. This is why people have a tendency to describe such systems as computer-aided *design* systems. In reality this is far from the truth. Today's CAD systems only serve to aid a small, but important, subset of the activities engaged in during the design of manufactured products.

The desire for more extensive computer-based support of the engineering design process has led to attempts to develop and extend the purely geometric representation techniques described above so that other types of design and manufacturing information can be represented. These attempts to *decorate* the geometric representations are proving to be of limited utility. The reason for this is primarily because making the representation of geometry the foundation onto which other types of design knowledge is attached leads to an inadequate representation scheme, both from a purely computational point of view and from an automatic reasoning point of view. For example, crawling (computationally) over a boundary or set-theoretic representation of a solid object hunting for features to be machined, the identification of which forms a necessary part of process planning, is proving to be computationally expensive, and conceptually inappropriate. What would be more appropriate, both conceptually and computationally, is the construction of a hierarchical representation which explicitly contains descriptions of the types of features (and possible subfeatures) which constitute the design and how they are functionally and spatially related, together with the description of their geometry. Such a hierarchical *feature-oriented* description would thus preserve information about the design that otherwise has to be reconstructed at considerable computational expense from a purely geometric, and thus explicitly *featureless*, description.

The idea of developing representation schemes specific to the different types of knowledge that need to be captured and recorded is one that is central to much of the knowledge representation work carried out under the label of artificial intelligence research. It is therefore appropriate to look to the knowledge representation and automatic reasoning techniques developed by AI research for ways in which to extend and enhance the computer-based support of the engineering design process.

AI-BASED DESIGN: A BRIEF REVIEW

Research into AI-based design started about ten years ago, but it is only in recent years that the subject has received significant attention. It is now a fast growing subfield of AI research with increasing numbers of research groups active within it.

The early work was carried out by Sussman *et al.* on systems for designing electrical and integrated circuits[11,12], Rich *et al.* on a system to support computer software design[13], and Latombe who was one of the first to consider the wider application of AI techniques to computer-aided design[14]. These early systems were based upon techniques for expressing design constraints and requirements in a mathematically precise way, and used constraint satisfaction techniques to prune the space of possible designs during an automated search process. From these early successes, AI-based design research began to develop in terms of three interdependent activities.

The first of these is concerned with the development of techniques for representing and reasoning about design knowledge in ways which can be used to support different types of design. Much of the current research effort in AI-based design is devoted to this activity which has led to proposals for what further techniques are required[15–20]. Work has also been carried out to develop tools which use knowledge-based system techniques to improve or enhance the usability of conventional computer-aided design techniques[21–30]. These developments are based upon a variety of AI techniques such as

- *blackboard* systems which link together numbers of different inferencing subsystems that reason about the same knowledge, or share it in some way (see the intelligent control section for more on this)
- *production rule* systems, sometimes called expert systems, which enable design knowledge to be encoded as rules that can be applied to domain knowledge to derive new facts or constraints about a design
- *structured object representation* systems that enable design knowledge to be structured in a hierarchical way, thus making it easier for a reasoning system to use knowledge expressed at the appropriate level of detail for a particular design activity, or stage, of the overall design task.

Systems which are aimed at specific design domains include: architecture[31,32], structural design[33–38], mechanical engineering[39,40], chemical engineering[41–43], control engineering[44], and electronic circuit design[45,46].

Some of this work has resulted in systems which can carry out complete designs automatically for specific, and often very limited, domains. They have represented in their knowledge bases sufficient domain knowledge to cover the range of designs required, the space of possible designs, together with heuristic knowledge about how the design process is to be carried out. They then use some kind of automated inferencing, or *reasoning*, technique to search the space of possible designs defined by the domain knowledge using the heuristic knowledge also encoded. While many of these systems sound impressive when reported in the literature, few of them have actually been used on a regular basis for real design problems. The best way to view these developments is not as systems which replace human designers, but as systems which can effectively carry out specific design tasks, which might form a critical, or laborious, aspect of a larger design task.

The second activity has been concerned with developing better models of the design process itself[47–57]. This is still a poorly understood aspect of engineering design. Consequently, how computer-based systems might be used to support all the activities engaged in by design engineers is also not well understood. The work on design models tends to be either concerned with the cognitive process which goes on in the minds of engineers when engaged in a design task, or the type and source of the knowledge used during design, and how it is manipulated. In either case, the building of AI-based, or knowledge-based, systems to support design tasks or to automate some of them is an important part of trying to develop better models of the design process.

Following the development of improved design process models and the initial testing of some basic techniques, a third research basic activity has more recently opened up on the integrated system architectures required by design support systems[56,58–66]. This work is principally concerned with what types of reasoning systems need to be coupled together and how they can be both automatically controlled and effectively interacted with by human users. The aim is to understand how effective and appropriate couplings of human and artificial intelligence can be achieved in design.

This system architecture research can also be seen as representing attempts to express current models of the design process in particular organizations of subsystems. This is necessary to test both the models and the various techniques used, as well as the system architectures. It is also an important part of improving our understanding of the engineering design process in general and how it can be intelligently supported in an integrated, coherent, and uniform manner.

Design support systems based upon the AI techniques so far developed are able to provide support for design at different levels of abstraction, the maintenance of dependency and consistency records across large amounts of design information, useful levels of automated reasoning to support laborious and tedious design tasks, and a sense of working *with* the designers rather than working *for* them.

ENGINEERING DESIGN

In order to provide a framework in which to discuss the ability of geometry-based techniques and AI-based techniques to support the engineering design process, an activity-based model of the design process will be described. This model sets out to represent the design process as a set of knowledge applying and knowledge generating activities which are engaged in during the process of design. It does not attempt to include any aspects of the human cognitive processes that also form part of the overall activity of design.

Engineering design is the process of going from the identification of a functional requirement to a specification of a product and its manufacture. At present there is not one generally agreed model of the design process. It is possible, however, to identify a set of basic types of knowledge applying and generating activities which are typically found in all kinds of engineering design. These activities include:

- Requirements description – in which the identified requirements are described or modelled in a formal or semiformal way, and modified as design possibilities and options are elaborated, incompletenesses identified, and inconsistencies discovered
- Decomposition – in which the requirements and thus the exploration task are broken down into more manageable subproblems
- Strategy planning – in which profitable orderings of intermediate design goals and subproblems are identified, with a view to the early determination of significant design features, and identification of difficulties
- Detailing and parameterization – in which parts of a design are worked on in detail to establish values, or bounds, on design parameters, performance estimates, manufacturing requirements, costs, etc.
- Synthesis – during which possible design schemes and solutions are generated from partial solutions of subproblems
- Simulation – during which the effectiveness of particular schemes or proposed mechanisms are investigated
- Analysis – during which the proposed design details, and parameter values and bounds, are tested against the requirements, and other criteria
- Optimization – during which the interactions and relationships between subparts of a design are optimized with respect to global requirement criteria
- Documentation – during which reasons for and explanations of design decisions and consequences are prepared and recorded

The result of the design process is a complete product specification, including its cost, manufacture, testing, documentation, installation, maintenance, repair, and even decommissioning or final disposal, etc.

The design process is, according to the model presented, progressed by engaging in a selection of the above activities in a hierarchical, iterative, and recursive, manner punctuated by occasional intuitive leaps, and the subsequent attempts to validate the results of such leaps. It is best seen as a process of *exploring* the space of possible designs. The structuring of the various activities carried out during this exploration reflects the necessary mixture of top-down and bottom-up approaches to engineering design.

During different phases of this exploration, different types of support will be required, corresponding to the different types of activity engaged in, and thus the different types of knowledge being applied and generated. As the exploration continues more and more, knowledge about the various possible design solutions will be accumulated and compared, until finally an acceptable design is found and, hopefully, validated.

AI-BASED DESIGN VERSUS GEOMETRY-BASED DESIGN

Based on the model of the design process presented in the previous section, a view of what types of functionality are required in a computer-based system to support the activities engaged in during the design process can be constructed. This computer-based functionality must be balanced against those activities that are best carried out by human designers so that in combination they lead to better quality designs produced with less human effort; in other words, a more efficient and complete exploration of the space of possible designs for a given amount of human effort.

There are four aspects of the design process which could benefit from computational support:

- knowledge representation
- mundane and/or laborious levels of reasoning
- consistency maintenance of the knowledge generated
- design process control

Each of these aspects will be considered in more detail, and the ability of AI-based and geometry-based techniques to support them will be discussed.

Knowledge representation

Some idea of the width and extent of the knowledge used during the design process is given by considering a typical design office in a mechanical engineering company. Depending upon the size of the company, there will be numbers of filing cabinets of loose-leaf printed and handwritten documentation and notes of previous designs; files of engineering drawings of previous and current jobs – either hard copy or computer-based CAD system files; engineering change note files; company, national, and international standards and regulations; component manufacturers' catalogues; textbooks and handbooks; the knowledge and experience of the people who work in the office; and access to other sources of knowledge, including people involved in other aspects of the engineered products.

To provide better computer-based support for the recording and accessing of this knowledge, the representation techniques used must meet two distinct needs. First, they must represent the engineering knowledge used during the design process, the *domain knowledge*, in a domain knowledge base (DKB). Second, they must represent and record the body of knowledge built up as a product is designed, the *task knowledge*, in a task knowledge base (TKB). Both of these types of knowledge require formal and expressive representation schemes, so that the wide variety of knowledge used to describe a product design and its manufacture, testing, maintenance, etc. can be built up and maintained. Here, *formal* means based upon an appropriate mathematical logic to which semantic meaning can be uniquely and consistently attached. This is so that it can support automated reasoning using logic-based inferencing techniques, as well as being able to express things in an unambiguous way. An *expressive* representation scheme is one that is able to represent a wide variety of types of objects and combinations of objects without becoming verbose in its constructions. This requirement can be likened to developments in modern computer programming languages which have become both more formal and more expressive compared to the first generation of high-level languages; they make it easier to instruct computers what we want them to do, and it is easier to check that the programs do what they are supposed to do.

One of the aims of AI-based engineering design support systems is to formally represent and integrate much of the knowledge used and generated during product design. By this means the informal knowledge management and maintenance, currently practised by design engineers, can be made a more formal process with associated formal methods for checking and validating the knowledge represented. This move towards a more disciplined approach to knowledge representation and management is a trend which can already be observed in a number of engineering design fields. VLSI design and software engineering are two particular examples. This trend is much less evident, though no less important, in the domain of mechanical engineering. While the geometry of a mechanical design is clearly important, depending upon a representation of it as a basis for the description of a design results in large amounts of knowledge about the design being lost. It may then have to be regenerated at a later stage, as in the example of feature hunting for process planning referred to in the section on geometry-based design.

At a conceptual level, this failure of geometry to provide a sound basis upon which to capture knowledge created during the design process is not surprising. During the early stages of the design process there is typically very little geometry established upon which to describe anything, but there are a lot of other types of knowledge being created in those early stages – such as the mechanisms to be used, the ranges of performance parameters, and material types and properties. It is important to recognize that what might be thought of as going on in a designer's head during the design process with respect to geometry cannot form a basis for a formal knowledge representation scheme to be implemented in a computer. The geometric ideas a designer may have gradually transform from purely notional ones to fully derived ones as the geometric shape parameters become fixed as a result of resolving and satisfying a wide range of different types of constraints during the design process. In other words, the geometric shape is the *result* of a constraints satisfaction process, not the *means* by which the constraints are satisfied. It cannot be the latter, because geometry cannot represent all the different types of constraints that have to be resolved, and so cannot provide the means for their resolution.

At a knowledge representation level, a well-drawn and annotated engineering drawing may provide a sufficient representation scheme for the communication of design knowledge between well-trained and experienced human designers, but it most certainly does not provide a satisfactory basis for the exchange of design knowledge between computer-based systems. Engineering drawings, even those produced according to established standards, are informal, ambiguous, and incomplete representations of designs. Their success as a knowledge representation scheme depends crucially upon the reasoning and interpretive skills of the human designers. These are skills that are not likely to be replicated in a computer-based system for many years, assuming that this is an appropriate thing to be trying to do, which it probably is not.

Thus, extending the support provided by present-day geometry-based CAD systems requires a significant extension to their knowledge representation capabilities beyond the geometry, or decorated geometry, representation schemes currently used. The development of expressive knowledge representation schemes forms one of the central activities of AI research, and it is to the results of these research activities that we must look for the required extensions of today's CAD systems.

Automated reasoning

Automated reasoning, or inferencing, techniques are required to support the different types of problem-solving activities engaged in as the space of possible designs is explored, and alternative designs are considered and compared. There are two different kinds of inferencing required.

The first kind requires forward inferencing procedural type techniques, to infer new knowledge from existing knowledge and to identify inconsistencies by extending paths in the relational structure maintained in the task knowledge base. For example, consider a situation in which a shaft is mounted in a casing using two roller bearings, and the relationships and constraints on the various dimensions are as follows:

$$\text{shaft1OuterDiameter} = \text{bearing1InnerDiameter} \tag{1}$$
$$\text{bearing1OuterDiameter}/\text{bearing1InnerDiameter} = 1.4 \tag{2}$$
$$\text{bearing1HousingDiameter} = \text{bearing1OuterDiameter} \tag{3}$$
$$\text{bearing1HousingDiameter} < 40\ \text{mm} \tag{4}$$

If shaft1OuterDiameter = 30 mm, then by substituting into the constraints (2) and (3) it can be inferred that

$$\text{bearing1HousingDiameter} = 42\ \text{mm}$$

This contradicts constraint (4) and such a contradiction should be brought to the notice of a designer. If this example is extended to include a second shaft to be mounted parallel to the first in the same casing, then we may have the following extra constraints:

$$\text{shaft2OuterDiameter} = \text{bearing2InnerDiameter} \tag{5}$$
$$\text{bearing2OuterDiameter}/\text{bearing2InnerDiameter} = 1.3 \tag{6}$$
$$\text{bearing2HousingDiameter} = \text{bearing2OuterDiameter} \tag{7}$$
$$\text{bearing2HousingDiameter} < 35\ \text{mm} \tag{8}$$
$$\text{minBearing1HousingWallThickness} = 15\ \text{mm} \tag{9}$$
$$\text{bearing1HousingWallThickness} > \text{minBearing1HousingWallThickness} \tag{10}$$
$$\text{minBearing2HousingWallThickness} = 13\ \text{mm} \tag{11}$$
$$\text{bearing2HousingWallThickness} > \text{minBearingHousingWallThickness} \tag{12}$$
$$\text{distanceBetweenShafts12} = \text{shaft1OuterDiameter} + \text{shaft2OuterDiameter} + 10\ \text{mm} \tag{13}$$
$$\text{distanceBetweenShafts12} > \text{minDistanceBetweenShafts12} \tag{14}$$
$$\text{minDistanceBetweenShafts12} = \text{bearing1HousingDiameter}/2 + \text{minBearing1HousingWallThickness} + \text{bearing2HousingDiameter}/2 + \text{minBearing2HousingWallThickness} \tag{15}$$

If shaft1OuterDiameter = 28 mm and shaft2OuterDiameter = 26 mm, then from constraints (2) and (3), and (6) and (7), respectively, bearing1HousingDiameter = 39.2 mm, and bearing2HousingDiameter = 33.8 mm.

From constraint (13) distanceBetweenShafts12 = 64 mm. However, from constraint (15) the minimum distance between the shafts is 64.5 mm, otherwise constraints (9) and (11) are contradicted.

This kind of *conflict* can be recognized by propagating values through the relational structure represented by constraint expressions, i.e. forward chaining, and by identifying the resulting inconsistency; that constraints (13) and (14) cannot both be satisfied if shaft1OuterDiameter = 28 mm and shaft2OuterDiameter = 26 mm, for example.

To resolve this conflict, one or other or both shaft diameters need to be modified. The decision as to what will be changed to resolve this situation is typically best left to the designer, though the consequences of any change should be traced through by the system, and this might lead to the identification of new conflicts.

To support mechanical design, forward-inferencing subsystems are required to support algebraic expression manipulation, equation solving, and value propagation (as illustrated above), and spatial relationship reasoning and geometric reasoning about space occupancy and shape.

The second kind of reasoning required is more amenable to backward-chaining rule-based techniques, and model-based qualitative reasoning techniques. For example, if an inferred value for the two bearing outer diameters is obtained in the above analysis, a rule relating bearing size to types of bearing available can be used by the system to reason from the desired bearing dimensions back to a particular bearing in a catalogue of available sizes. Or, if the system has a model representing the causal relationships between the loading on a bearing, its average running speed, and bearing wear, the system might be able to infer the expected life of a bearing given a specific loading and running speed. The same model might also be used to infer a recommended average running speed, given a specific loading and wear characteristics, in a different situation.

These backward-chaining and model-based reasoning techniques can be used to build subsystems to advise designers about particular aspects of a design, or support the assessment, or analysis, of a design, or the meeting of some intermediate design goal, by applying rules to items of knowledge found in the task knowledge base. Backward-chaining systems can be used to support the more directed, and specialist, types of activity in the design process; for example, design requirements identification and description, design task decomposition, component and materials selection, the application of standard design procedures, design assessment and analysis, formal design review procedures, and manfacture design and planning.

The provision of such automated reasoning support to designers depends on having a design support system architecture very different from that of today's CAD systems which are based upon solid modelling or more simple 3D modelling systems. They also require the expressive knowledge representation schemes described above. It is not possible to provide these types of reasoning capabilities if only a geometric representation of a design is maintained.

Consistency maintenance

As the design process proceeds, and a body of knowledge is built up in the task knowledge base, the dependencies between elements of that knowledge, and their consistency, have to be recorded and maintained – like those illustrated in the previous section. This is so that, as new knowledge is added or new design decisions and choices are made, the relationships they have on all existing aspects of the design so far described can be discovered, and the designer informed at an early stage of any constraint violations and inconsistencies introduced into the design description as a result. The violation of the constraint on the minimum distance between the two shafts, in the example above, is an instance of this kind of inconsistency. Occurrences of this kind of situation are a natural consequence of the exploratory nature of the design process, where different possibilities will need to be considered, and possibly compared.

In order to investigate how the constraint violation, identified by the forward inferencing described in the previous section, might be resolved, a range of different values for shaft1OuterDiameter and shaft2OuterDiameter might be tried. These trial values constitute different possible designs. We might therefore have a situation as follows:

Design 1	shaft1OuterDiameter = 28 mm
	shaft2OuterDiameter = 28 mm
Design 2	shaft1OuterDiameter = 30 mm
	shaft2OuterDiameter = 26 mm
Design 3	shaft1OuterDiameter = 31 mm
	shaft2OuterDiameter = 25 mm

All three designs are consistent with constraints (1–15). But unless the system knew that the three pairs of values for shaft1OuterDiameter and shaft2OuterDiameter were associated with three distinct designs, it could use any combination in its forward inferencing. Though perfectly correct logically, this would clearly lead to nonsensical information being generated. It is therefore necessary for the system to record the fact that the pairs of values for shaft1OuterDiameter and shaft2OuterDiameter for each of the three designs are inconsistent with each other, and so should not be used in any other combinations for inferring new values for other parameters in the relational structure.

The AI techniques most suitable for dealing with this type of problem are described as truth maintenance techniques[67,68], assumption-based truth maintenance systems (ATMS)[69] being of particular relevance to design support problems.

Currently available design support systems barely acknowledge the existence of the problem of consistency maintenance, which is the generalization of the version control problem. This failure represents what is perhaps the single most serious inadequacy of today's CAD

ystems. Providing consistency maintenance support
teams of designers working together on a large design
roject is as yet an unsolved problem requiring further
search. However, what is already clear from the
-based design research carried out to date is that
roviding such a capability has important implications
r the architecture of design support systems, and the
ay they are implemented.

telligent control

central difference between the geometry-based
sign support systems currently available and AI-
sed systems of the future is that the geometry-based
stems offer *passive* support, whereas AI-based system
ll offer *active* support. In other words, AI-based
stems offer *passive* support, whereas AI-based systems
nerated during the process of design, but will also
ke an active part in that process via the automatic
vocation of intelligent subsystems and consistency
aintenance systems. It is by this means that a better
d more effective combination of human and computer-
sed activities to solve complex engineering problems
ll be sought. To do this will require a level of system
ntrol well above that typically found in current CAD
stems, which only have to respond directly to human
out commands, albeit sometimes slowly.

The integrated control of the invocation and
eractions between a set of intelligent subsystems to
liver flexible and uniform support to engineers engaged
a design task is an old problem in the field of AI.
wever, there are a number of promising techniques
ose extensions to meet these requirements are being
estigated. These techniques come under the general
els of blackboard control models[70,71], and context
ering techniques[72].

The blackboard control model provides a structured
y of combining a number of different reasoning
tems in such a way that they can work together
portunistically to solve problems. Metaphorically we
n think of a set of workers, all looking at the same
ckboard: each is able to read everything that is on
and to judge when he or she has something
rthwhile to add to it[73]. In this way a solution to a
blem is gradually built up on the blackboard by the
lective actions of all the workers. For example, in a
tem to support mechanical design we might have
arate subsystems able to reason about algebraic
nstraint expressions, spatial relationship descriptions
how parts fit together), geometric space occupancy
d shape descriptions, and tabulated data, such as
aring catalogues and empirically derived wear
aracteristics of bearings. The work of each of these
soning subsystems is recorded in the same data
ucture, called the blackboard, and each is able to
cess all items of interest, and decide for itself when
an do anything with any of it. The blackboard system
hitecture is one of the oldest intelligent control
hitectures developed by AI research, and it has been
d in a number of the most successful AI-based
tems. Its use in AI-based design support systems is
without its problems, however, and these need to
the subject of further research. One particularly
difficult problem concerns the overall control of the
support systems behaviour. To support designers
effectively the systems reasoning must be directed
towards the task the designers are engaged in. For the
system to do this it must have knowledge of what the
task is and how it is to be carried out. Requirements
modelling and user modelling are the areas of AI
research which are concerned with these kinds of
problems.

Context layering, or context management, is another
way of effecting an appropriate relationship between
designers and a design support system. It provides a
way of expressing to the system the structure of the
design process. This not only helps designers to be more
disciplined, but also provides more information to the
system about the task it is supposed to be supporting.
It also provides a means by which design support
systems can manage the complexity of a complete
design task, which is something people are typically
not very good at.

This requirement for more sophisticated kinds of
control also has deep implications for the design
of design support systems architectures and their
implementation. None of the techniques described in
this section could be effectively implemented in today's
CAD system architectures: they have not been designed
to actively support the full range of design activities,
but only to act as a passive aid to certain aspects of
the overall task.

CONCLUDING REMARKS

Today's computer-aided drafting systems, and associated
analysis programs, are only able to support a subset of
the activities listed in the engineering design section
and a limited representation of the product design
description. This has led to a sequentially organized
model of design support, which results in the
fragmentation of the design process and the consequent
distribution and loss of knowledge during the design
and manufacture of a product[56].

It is argued that current geometry-based design
support systems (CAD systems) are inherently limited
in their ability to meet the needs of the more powerful
and wide ranging design support systems required to
more closely integrate engineering design activities, and
that it is these limitations that have motivated research
into AI-based design support systems.

The AI-based design research being carried out at
the Department of Artificial Intelligence, Edinburgh
University, UK, is seeking to develop a novel approach
to the support of engineering design based upon the
ideas presented in the previous sections. This approach
models design as an accumulation of a coherent body
of knowledge about a particular product and the
process of its design resulting from the exploration of
the space of possible designs: as more space is explored
more knowledge is accumulated. This knowledge
represents both descriptions and specifications of
possible designs and their manufacture, and a record
of the exploration process itself in terms of the activities
engaged in and their relational dependencies and
ordering.

A system to support the design process modelled in this way has not only to support the different types of design activity, but also to record and maintain the large body of knowledge generated. To do this in an integrated and flexible way requires the tight coupling of a number of subsystems which make use of various AI techniques. These techniques include knowledge representation, formal reasoning, consistency management, and intelligent system control.

The aim of AI-based design support systems is to provide an effective degree of automated reasoning and consistency management so that these traditionally human tasks can be taken over by the computer-based system, thus releasing designers from what are typically tedious and stressful activities. This leaves designers to concentrate more effectively on problem-specific questions raised by a particular design task. By this means better quality design will be achieved.

ACKNOWLEDGEMENTS

The research being carried out into AI-based design support systems at the Department of Artificial Intelligence, Edinburgh University, UK (EDAI), is funded by a grant from the UK Science and Engineering Research Council, and forms part of the Alvey large scale demonstrator project *Design to Product*, other parts of which are funded by GEC plc, Lucas Diesel Systems Ltd, and the Department of Trade and Industry. The ideas and opinions expressed here have been developed over a number of years and have benefited from numerous discussions with other members of the Edinburgh Designer System team which has included Professor Robin Popplestone, Steve Todd, Anastasia Koutsou, Gideon Sahar, Robert Gray, Dominic Prior, Jonathan Corney; and currently includes Karl Millington, Alistair Conkie, Jim Doheny, Andy Robertson, and Lorraine Martin. I also wish to express thanks to other members of the EDAI Advanced Robotics group: Chris Malcolm, John Hallam, Professor Jim Howe, and Wade Troxell (visiting from Colorado State University, USA), who have read and usefully commented on earlier versions of this paper.

REFERENCES

1 **Sutherland, I E, Sproull, R F and Schumacker, R A** 'A characterisation of ten hidden-surface algorithms' *ACM Comput. Surv.* Vol 6 No 1 (1974) pp 1–55

2 **Rogers, D F and Adams, J A** *Mathematical elements for computer graphics* McGraw-Hill, London, UK (1976)

3 **Braid, I C** 'Geometric modelling – ten years on' *CAD Group Document No 103* University of Cambridge, Computer Laboratory, Cambridge, UK (1979)

4 **Baer, A, Eastman, C and Henrion, M** 'Geometric modelling: a survey' *Comput.-Aided Des.* Vol 11 No 5 (1979) pp 253–72

5 **Faux, I D and Pratt, M J** *Computational geometry for design and manufacture* Ellis Horwood, Chichester, UK (1979)

6 **Requicha, A A G** 'Representations of rigid solids: theory, methods and systems' *ACM Comput. Surv.* Vol 12 No 4 (1980) pp 437–64

7 **Requicha, A A G and Voelcker, H B** 'Solid modelling: a historical summary and contemporary assessment' *IEEE Comput. Graph. Appl.* (March 1982)

8 **Foley, J D and Van Dam, A** *Fundamentals of interactive computer graphics* Addison Wesley, Reading, MA, USA (1982)

9 **Willis, P J** 'A review of recent hidden surface removal techniques' *Displays* Vol 6 No 1 (1985) pp 11–20

10 **Woodwark, J** *Computing shape* Butterworths, Guildford, UK (1986)

11 **Sussman, G J** 'Electrical design, a problem for artificial intelligence research' *AI Memo No 425* MIT AI Laboratory, Massachusetts Institute of Technology, Cambridge, MA, USA (1977)

12 **Sussman, G J, Holloway, J and Knight, T F Jr** 'Computer aided evolutionary design for digital integrated systems' *AI Memo No 526* MIT AI Laboratory, Massachusetts Institute of Technology, Cambridge, MA, USA (1979)

13 **Rich, C, Shrobe, H E and Waters, R C** 'Computer aided evolutionary design for software engineering' *AI Memo No 506* MIT AI Laboratory, Massachusetts Institute of Technology, Cambridge, MA, USA (1979)

14 **Latombe, J-C** 'Artificial intelligence in computer-aided design: the 'Tropic' system' *Technical Note 125* Stanford Research Institute Artificial Intelligence Center, Stanford, CA, USA (1976)

15 **Maher, M L, Sriram, D and Fenves, S J** 'Tools and techniques for knowledge based expert systems for engineering design' *Adv. Eng. Softw.* Vol 6 No 4 (1984) pp 178–188

16 **Hatvany, J** 'The missing tools of CAD for mechanical engineering' in **Gero, J S (ed.)** *Knowledge engineering in computer-aided design* Elsevier North-Holland, Amsterdam, The Netherlands (1985)

17 **Tomiyama, T and Yoshikawa, H** 'Requirements and principles for intelligent CAD systems' in **Gero, J S (ed.)** *Knowledge engineering in computer-aided design* Elsevier North-Holland, Amsterdam, The Netherlands (1985)

18 **Brotchie, J F, Sharpe, R and Marksjo, B** 'Introducing intelligence and knowledge into CAD' in **Sriram, D and Adey, R (eds)** *Applied AI in Engineering Problems, 1st Int. Conf.* Vol 2 Springer, Southampton, UK (1986) pp 797–810

19 **Dixon, J R** 'Artificial intelligence and design: a mechanical engineers view' *Proc. AAAI-86 5th Nat. Conf. on AI* Vol 2 (1986) pp 872–877

20 **Stoll, H W** 'Artificial intelligence and mechanical design: possibilities and problems' *Ultratech. Conf. Proc.* Vol 1 (1986) pp 225–236

Sandewall, E 'A survey of artificial intelligence with special respect to computer-aided design' in **Latombe, J C (ed.)** *AI and pattern recognition in computer aided design* IFIP North-Holland, Amsterdam, The Netherlands (1978) pp 19–34

Rychener, M D 'Expert systems for engineering design: experiments with basic techniques' *Proc. of Trends and Applications on Automating Intelligent Behaviour: Applications and Frontiers* (1983) pp 21–27

Barbuceanu, M 'Object-centred representation and reasoning: an application to computer-aided design' *SIGART Newsletter* Vol 87 (1984) pp 33–39

Swift, K G, Matthews, A and Syan, C S 'Artificial intelligence in engineering design' *Proc. CAM-I 13th Annual Meeting and Technical Conf.* Clearwater Beach, FL, USA (1984) pp 13–15

MacCallum, K J, Duffly, A and Green, S 'An intelligent concept design assistant' in *IFIP W.G.5.2. Working Conf. on Design Theory for CAD* Tokyo, Japan (1985) North-Holland, New York, NY, USA (1987) pp 233–249

Mitchell, T M, Steinberg, A D and Shulman, J S 'A knowledge based approach to design' *IEEE Trans. Pattern Anal. Mach. Intell.* Vol PAMI-7 No 5 (1985) pp 502–510

Chalfan, K M 'A knowledge system that integrates heterogeneous software for a design application' *AI Mag.* Vol 7 No 2 (1986) pp 80–84

Chan, W T 'Logic programming for managing constant-based engineering design' *PhD Thesis* Department of Civil Engineering, Stanford University, Stanford, CA, USA (1986)

Maher, M L and Longinos, P 'Development of an expert system shell for engineering design' *EDRC-12-05-86* Engineering Design Research Center, Carnegie Mellow University, Pittsburgh, PA, USA (1985)

Rehak, D R and Howard, H C 'Interfacing expert systems with design databases in integrated CAD systems' *EDRC-12-01-86* Engineering and Design Research Center, Carnegie Mellon University, Pittsburgh, PA, USA (1986)

Gero, J S, Radford, A D, Coyne, R and Akiner, V T 'Knowledge-based computer-aided architectural design' in **Gero, J S (ed.)** *Knowledge engineering in computer-aided design* Elsevier North Holland, Amsterdam, The Netherlands (1985)

Monoghan, P F and Doheny, J G 'Knowledge representation in the conceptual design process for building energy systems' in **Sriram, D and Adey, R (eds)** *Applied AI in Engineering Problems 1st Int. Conf.* Vol 2 Springer, Southampton, UK (1986) pp 1187–1192

Fenves, S J and Norabhoompipat, T 'Potential for artificial intelligence applications in structural engineering design and detailing' in **Latombe, J C (ed.)** *AI and Pattern Recognition in Computer Aided Design* IFIP North-Holland, Amsterdam, The Netherlands (1978) pp 105–122

34 **Bennett, J, Creary, L, Engelmore, R and Melosh, R** 'SACON: a knowledge based consultant for structural analysis' *Proc. 6th IJCAI* (1979) pp 47–49

35 **Farinacci, M L, Fox, M S, Hulthage, I and Rychener, M D** 'The development of Aladin, an expert system for aluminium alloy design' *Proc. Conf. Artificial Intelligence in Manufacturing Key to Integration?* Gottlieb Dutweiler Institute, Zurich, Switzerland (November 1985)

36 **Fenves, S J and Sriram, D** 'DESTINY: A knowledge-based approach to integrated structural design' *SIGART Newsletter* No 92 (1985) pp 66–67

37 **Karakatsanis, A G** 'Floder, a floor designer expert system' *MSc Thesis* Department of Civil Engineering, Carnegie Mellon University, Pittsburgh, PA, USA (1985)

38 **Sriram, D** *Knowledge based approach to integrated structural design* CML Publications, Ashurst, UK (1985)

39 **Chao, N** 'Application of a knowledge based system to design for manufacture' *IEEE Int. Conf. on Robotics and Automation* (March 1985) pp 182–185

40 **Miller, A S and Hannam, R G** 'Computer aided design using a knowledge base approach and its application to the design of jigs and fixtures' *Proc. Inst. Mech. Eng.* Vol 199 No B4 (1985) pp 227–234

41 **Sriram, D, Banares-Alcantara, R, Venkatasubramanaian, V, Westerberg, A and Rychener, M** *Knowledge-based expert systems: an emerging technology for CAD in chemical engineering* Engineering Design Research Center, Carnegie Mellon University, Pittsburgh, PA, USA (1986)

42 **Lien, K, Suzuki, G and Westerberg, A W** 'The role of expert systems technology in design' *EDRC-06-13-86* Department of Chemical Engineering and Design Research Center, Carnegie Mellon University, Pittsburgh, PA, USA (1986)

43 **Banares-Alcantara, R** 'Decade: a hybrid knowledge-based system for catalyst selection' *PhD Thesis* Department of Chemical Engineering, Carnegie Mellon University, Pittsburgh, PA, USA (1986)

44 **Nolan, P J** 'An intelligent assistant for control system design' in **Sriram, D and Adey, R (eds)** *Applied AI in Engineering Problems, 1st Int. Conf.* Vol 1 Springer, Southampton, UK (1986) pp 473–481

45 **McDermott, D** 'Circuit design as problem solving' in **Lacombe, J C (ed.)** *AI and pattern recognition in computer aided design* IFIP North-Holland, Amsterdam, The Netherlands (1978) pp 227–260

46 **Steinberg, L I and Mitchell, T M** 'A knowledge based approach to VLSI CAD – the REDESIGN system' *ACM IEEE 21st Design Automation Conf. Proc.* Albuquerque, NM, USA (June 1984) pp 412–418

47 **Preiss, K** 'Engineering design viewed as an activity in artificial intelligence' *SRI International Technical Note 167* Stanford Research Institute, Stanford, CA, USA (1978)

48 **Malhotra, A, Thomas, J C, Carroll, J M and Miller, L A** 'Cognitive processes in design' *Int. J. Man-Mach. Stud.* (1980) pp 119–140

49 **Yoshikawa, H** 'General design theory and CAD systems', in **Sata, T and Warman, E (eds)** *Man–machine communication in CAD/CAM Proc. IFIP WG 5.2-5.3 Working Conf.* Tokyo, Japan (1980) North-Holland, Amsterdam, The Netherlands (1980) pp 35–58

50 **Eastman, C M** 'Recent developments in representation in the science of design' *Proc. IEEE 18th Conf. Design Automation* (1981) pp 13–21

51 **Rooney, M F and Smith, S E** 'Artificial intelligence in engineering design' *Comput. Struct.* Vol 16 No 1-4 (1982) pp 279–288

52 **Whitefield, A** 'A model of the engineering design process derived from HEARSEY-II' *1st IFIP Conf. Human–Computer Interaction* Vol 1 Elsevier, Amsterdam, The Netherlands (1984) pp 424–428

53 **Bijl, A** 'An approach to design theory' in *IFIP W.G.5.2. Working Conf. on Design Theory for CAD* Tokyo, Japan (1985) North-Holland, New York, NY, USA (1987) pp 1–23

54 **Kramer, G A** 'Representing and reasoning about designs' in *IFIP WG.5.2 Working Conf. on Design Theory for CAD* Tokyo, Japan (1985) North-Holland, New York, NY, USA (1987) pp 45–74

55 **Mostow, J** 'Towards better models of the design process' *AI Mag.* (Spring 1985) pp 44–56

56 **Smithers, T** 'The Alvey large scale demonstrator project 'Design to Product'' *Proc. Conf. Artificial Intelligence in Manufacturing Key to Integration?* Gottlieb Dutweiler Institute, Zurich, Switzerland (November 1985)

57 **Coyne, R D** 'A logic model of design synthesis' *PhD Thesis* Department of Architectural Science, University of Sydney, Sydney, Australia (1986)

58 **Dixon, J R, Simmons, M K and Cohen, P R** 'An architecture for application of artificial intelligence to design' *Proc ACM IEEE 21st Design Automation Conf.* (1984) pp 634–640

59 **Rychener, M D** 'A rule-based blackboard kernal system: some principles in design' *Proc. IEEE Workshop on Principles of Knowledge Based Systems* Denver, CO, USA (1984) pp 59–64

60 **Brown, D C and Chandrasekaran, B** 'Expert systems for a class of mechanical design activity' in **Gero, J S (ed.)** *Knowledge engineering in computer-aided design* Elsevier North-Holland, Amsterdam, The Netherlands (1985)

61 **Fox, M S and Baykan, C A** 'WRIGHT: an intelligent CAD system' *SIGART Newsletter, Special section on AI in engineering* No 92 (1985) pp 61–62

62 **Ohsuga, S** 'Conceptual design of CAD systems involving knowledge bases' in **Gero, J S (ed.)** *Knowledge engineering in computer-aided design* Elsevier North-Holland, Amsterdam, The Netherlands (1985)

63 **Rehak, D R, Craig, H and Sriram, D** 'Architecture of an integrated knowledge based environment for structural engineering applications' in **Gero, J S (ed.)** *Knowledge engineering in computer-aided design* Elsevier North-Holland, Amsterdam, The Netherlands (1985)

64 **Popplestone, R J, Smithers, T, Corney, J, Koutsou, A, Millington, K and Sahar, G** 'Engineering design support systems' *DAI Research Paper No 286* Department of Artificial Intelligence, Edinburgh University, Edinburgh, UK (1986)

65 **Corby, O** 'Blackboard architectures in computer aided engineering' *AI in Eng.* Vol 1 No 2 (1986) pp 95–98

66 **Mittal, S and Araya, A** 'A knowledge-based framework for design' *Proc. AAAI Conf.* (1986) pp 856–865

67 **McAllester, D A** 'A three-valued truth maintenance system' *Technical Report Memo 473* MIT AI Laboratory, Massachusetts Institute of Technology, Cambridge, MA, USA (1978)

68 **Doyle, J** 'A truth maintenance system' *Artif. Intell.* Vol 12 No 3 (1979) pp 231–272

69 **de Kleer, J** 'Choices without backtracking' *Proc. AAAI-84* (1984) pp 79–85

70 **Nii, P** 'Blackboard systems part one – the blackboard model of problem solving and the evolution of blackboard architectures' *AI Mag.* Vol 7 No 2 (1986) pp 38–53

71 **Nii, P** 'Blackboard systems part two – blackboard applications systems, blackboard systems from a knowledge engineering perspective' *AI Mag.* Vol 7 No 3 (1986) pp 82–106

72 **Worden, R P** 'Context in knowledge bases' *Working paper from 2nd meeting of the Alvey Working Group on Large Knowledge Based Systems: Computational Machines Interfaces* (November 1984)

73 **Newell, A** 'Some problems of basic organisation in problem-solving programs' in **Yovits, M C, Jacobi, G T and Goldstein, G D (eds)** *Conference on self-organizing systems* Spartan Books, Washington, DC, USA (1962)

NOREMA DESIGN: A Knowledge Based System for Kitchen Design

M. Kloster, J.C. Gjerløw and O. Ohren
Department of Knowledge Based Systems, Center for Industrial Research, Oslo, Norway

INTRODUCTION

Norema Design is an interactive knowledge based system for the design of kitchen floorplan layouts. A prototype system has been developed. The system is currently under development and an online version is to be installed by summer 1989.

Norema Design designs kitchens by applying a top-down strategy. Starting with an empty kitchen, *Norema Design* first identifies the layout for the kitchen interior as a whole. Then the interior is filled out with kitchen cabinets, forming the final design of the kitchen interior as suggested by the system. The major reasoning formalisms used at the different stages of the design process, are procedural reasoning , rule-based reasoning and constraint propagation.

Norema Design is being developed in cooperation with Norema Ltd., Norway's largest manufacturer of kitchen interiors. The users of the system will be Norema's sales staff, inexperienced in designing kitchen floorplans. Presently, a CAD system is used by the Norema sales staff for drawing kitchen floorplan layouts for their customers. Since this is a mere drafting system, the knowledge needed to design kitchens has to be possessed by the user. In many of the retail stores, however, there is a lack of professional designers. In order to distribute expert knowledge on kitchen design, Norema has decided to develop *Norema Design*. The system will be integrated with the existing CAD system and act as a supplement to this.

Norema Design is basically a generative system, another example of which is described in Fox[6]. An alternative approach is to support kitchen design by a computer system acting as a design critic. Examples of such systems are given in Oxman[10] and Fischer[5]. Issues within knowledge based design in general, are McDermott[8], and Magee[9].

ISSUES IN KITCHEN DESIGN

The basic idea in kitchen manufacturing today is to produce a set of standard cabinets and accessories, see figure 1, which shows some of Norema's kitchen products. Together with certain electrical appliances this set forms the total set from which one may choose and assemble a kitchen interior. In the following, the term <u>module</u> is to be interpreted as any element of the total set.

<u>The kitchen design task</u> may be defined as follows:
Given the exact geometry of the interior as a whole, design the interior layout by:

- selecting modules from a given, finite set of modules.
  (The <u>selection task</u>)
- positioning the chosen modules correctly within the geometric constraints, conforming to the functional and aesthetic demands of the kitchen owner.
  (The <u>configuration task</u>)

Kitchen design is characterized by a strong component of personal taste, as well as relatively frequent changes (mainly due to changes in the manufacturers' product range). The design knowledge is heuristic in nature, the greater part of the knowledge is formulated as advisory rules-of-thumb rather than absolute requirements. A significant feature of these rules is the frequent use of <u>symbols</u> in stead of numbers, e.g. "In <u>large</u> kitchens, we usually include a cabinet with towel bars", "The range should not be placed <u>too close to</u> the sink".

A computer system performing a task within a domain having the above mentioned features,has to satisfy certain requirements concerning representation and processing of knowledge. Such requirements include the need for a representational formalism that makes it easy to add new knowledge to the system, the ability to separate domain specific knowledge from the rest of the program, and the ability to manipulate symbols. It seems clear that these requirements are better taken care of by utilizing programming methods and techniques from the KBS (Knowledge Based Systems) technology, than by conventional (exclusively procedural) programming.

The problem of kitchen design is intrinsically under-constrained. For many of the above modules there are not sufficiently many rules to decide exactly when to select them and where to place them. Our observations of human designers at work strongly indicate that the actual inclusion of such modules in a kitchen plan is a result of deep knowledge rather than analytical behavior. In the system, the designers' seemingly random choices are replaced by systematic rules, which in many respects form a body of new design knowledge.

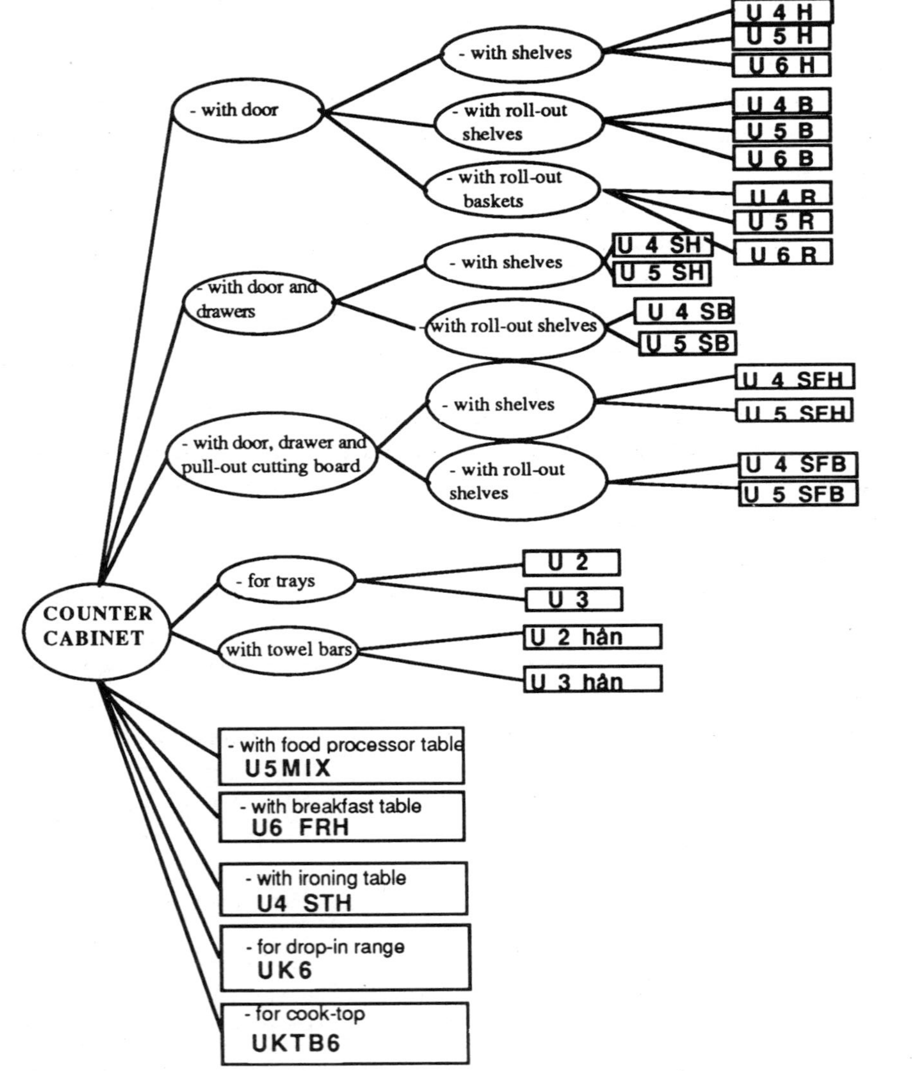

Figure 1. A subset of counter cabinets currently available from Norema. Rectangles denote individuals (cabinet types), whereas ovals denote classes of cabinet types.

Knowledge Acquisition

To acquire the knowledge, we cooperated with two design experts. Using more than one expert was mainly motivated by the subjective nature of the domain, making it easier to detect discrepancies and subjectivities. Discussions elucidated misunderstandings and inconsistencies.

The knowledge acquisition took place as interviews where the expert designed carefully chosen kitchen examples. The example set was assembled by systematically varying parameters important for the kitchen design. Such parameters are for instance: positioning and geometry of fan outlet, plumbing, doors, and windows, the size of the kitchen, customer requests etc. While designing, the expert explained his/her reasoning and thereby articulated the "rules" he/she made use of. A total of twelve interviews gave about forty kitchen floorplan layouts as a result. All interviews were recorded, leaving the knowledge engineers to spend their efforts in observing the expert during his/her work. The experts showed a great interest for the work, and this way of acquiring knowledge turned out to be very successful. A total of about five hundred written pages resulted from the taped interviews, which became the basis of the systems knowledge.

THE SYSTEM

Norema Design is highly interactive and flexible and works as a design workbench for the user. At any stage in the consultation, the user may go back to previous stages and choose different paths (specifications) from there in order to see the effects of this on the design of the kitchen.

The system is being developed on a Xerox 1186 Lisp machine using Epitool/DE for implementing the knowledge base. Epitool/DE is a hybrid tool which facilitates a combination of rule based, object oriented and conventional procedural programming techniques. The user interface is implemented in Lisp. The runtime version of Epitool, Epitool/EE (Execution Environment), allows porting the compiled version of *Norema Design* to a PC. This porting facility is of course of great importance to Norema since PCs running the CAD system are already in use at many of their retail stores.

The most significant features of the user interface, is the use of windows, menus and graphics. All input from the user is given by choosing from menus and/or by pointing. The complete *Norema Design* will communicate with existing systems used by Norema Ltd. The major interface will be with a 3D CAD-system, and

Xerox 1186 will be used for maintenance and further development, the Lisp interface will have to be maintained also in the future.

System Architecture

The architecture of *Norema Design* is shown in figure 2. The system consists of the following 4 main parts:

1. A dynamic solution space. Here, the system's representation of the kitchen and the solutions are constructed and kept during a consultation (figure 3).

2. The knowledge base incorporating expert knowledge on kitchen design. The knowledge base is subdivided into four modules: Outline Layout Module, Design Module, Design Modification Module, and the Control Module. Included in the knowledge base is also the rule inference mechanism.

3. A database describing Norema's kitchen products.

4. User interface.

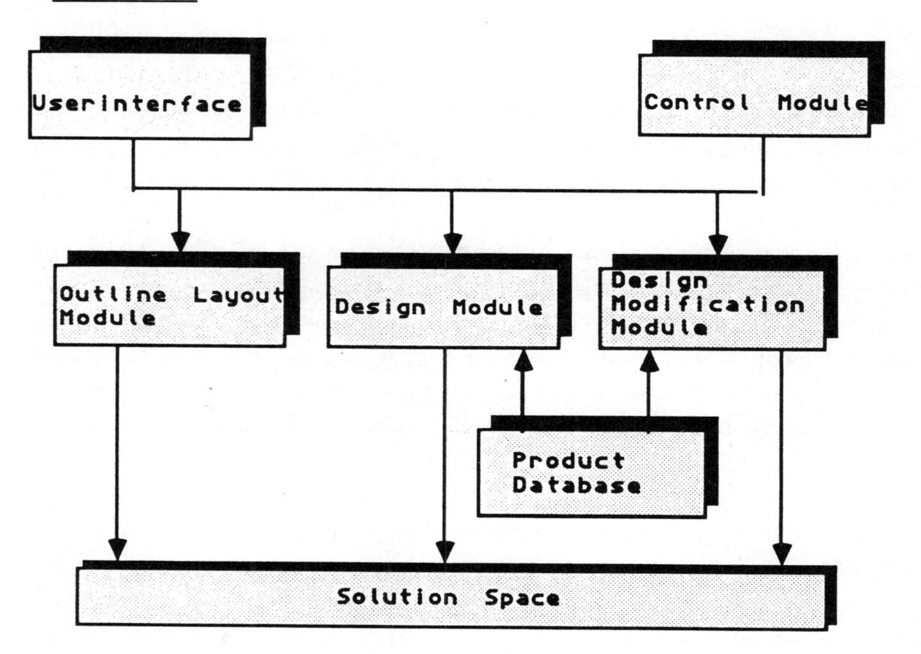

Figure 2. The architecture of the system and how the different parts interact.

This section gives a description of the most important terms used throughout the rest of the paper.

Room Constraint Room constraints may affect the design of the interior in a kitchen. A room constraint may be a: door, window, plumbing, fan outlet, fire wall, radiator, projection, opening (instead of a door), eating area, or something unspecified (user specified area). A constraint may be associated with one or more walls or with no wall at all, e.g. the fan outlet can be located on a wall or in the ceiling in the middle of the room.

Kitchen A kitchen consists of any number of walls and a minimum of two room constraints: there has to be at least one door or an opening as well as plumbing in the kitchen. The angle between two walls may be between 90 and 270. The walls do not necessarily have to be connected, that is; there may be openings in the kitchen. The minimum number of walls in a kitchen is one.

Outline of Interior This is the outline of the interior as a whole, without the specific modules placed into it. There are separate outlines for the counter cabinets and wall cabinets. The outline usually runs along the walls in the kitchen, forming the geometric shape of the interior. Peninsulas but not islands are allowed in the present version. In this paper, "outline" instead of outline of interior is sometimes used for short.

Maximum Outline of Interior All areas along the walls where it is allowed to place wall cabinets or counter cabinets. The outline of interior is a subset of the maximum outline of interior.

Design of Interior This is an outline of interior filled with modules, that is, a designed kitchen. Sometimes only the word "design" is used to describe this.

Module A module is defined in the previous section.

Open Space This represents an area in the outline of an interior not filled with modules. This term is only used during the design process in order to be able to express partial design solutions.

Making a Kitchen Design

This section gives an explanation of how a kitchen design is derived by *Norema Design* and how things are represented in the system. The description is seen mainly from the system's point of view. The section starts by going through the different kinds of design knowledge needed to make a design and how this is represented in the system. Next, an explanation of how *Norema Design* with the assistance from the user finds a design suggestion by going through 4 main design stages is given.

First a few words about the representation used: because of the diversity of the knowledge needed to design a kitchen floorplan, several representation and reasoning formalisms have been used in the system, namely object-oriented-, rule-based-, and function-based formalisms. These formalisms are all offered by Epitool/DE. The objects are representated in a specialization IS-A taxonomy with inheritance, forming a network of individuals with attributes and methods.

Representation of the Knowledge Due to the nature of the problem domain, the most important consideration when choosing representation has been to separate design specific knowledge from the deduction mechanisms and to represent this knowledge as explicitly as possible. This is done in order to ease the maintenance of the knowledge base.

The knowledge needed to perform the design task (defined in the previous chapter), is mainly centered around the modules. The most fundamental information about a module are geometrical facts (width, height, etc.), functional facts (what function the module usually has in a kitchen) , and its relations (in terms of module taxonomy) to other modules. This forms the basis for the task-specific knowledge about the modules.

Concerning selection, most of the knowledge deals with selecting modules belonging to category 3 (see Stage 3... in later section), i.e. dealing with when to select a module for a design and when not to. The chosen representation for this knowledge is rules organized in sets. Both backward rules and forward rules are used.

As for the configuration task, the requirements and recommendations concerning where to place the modules, i.e. the positioning constraints, are expressed using predicates forming spatial relations between modules and other objects (modules, room constraints, or fixed locations in the outline). Only binary relations are used. positioning constraint is: "The range should not be placed In-Front-Of a window." The constraints are represented as objects organized in an IS-A taxonomy. The constraints are ranked according to relative importance for the quality of the solution, which is used during the design process. A set of positioning constraints are associated with each module type.

The design process is described algorithmically, that is, a general design procedure applicable in all cases is identified and implemented. However, well-defined subproblems (e.g. decide whether a certain module should be included, or find the best position for a selected module) are delegated to rules or the constraint handling mechanism.

The remaining part of this section describes how *Norema Design* finds a kitchen design. The basic idea is a top-down development of a solution. The partial solutions are developed through generation of the search tree, which represents the design strategy used in *Norema Design*. Heuristics are used for pruning purposes. The process is illustrated in figure 3, through a visualization of the solution space, which contains all partial and final design solutions generated by the system. In the following, each stage will be described with respect to the solutions derived in the stage, and the inference methods used.

Stage 1: Describing the Kitchen

The purpose of this first stage is to get a description of the kitchen from the user and to represent it in the system. The description, which consists of the geometric layout of the kitchen as well as the room constraints, is entirely based on user specifications, together with a few consistency checks performed by the system. Examples of the latter are: "Is there at least one opening or door into the room?" and "Is there marked any plumbing in the kitchen?" The user gives the input by marking all the corner points of the kitchen as well as the room constraints on the screen with the mouse.

The kitchen is represented as an object. A kitchen consists of any number of walls and room constraints, all represented as objects. A wall individual contains geometrical information, e.g. angles to the adjacent walls, and coordinates. An individual of a room constraint contains information on location, relations to other

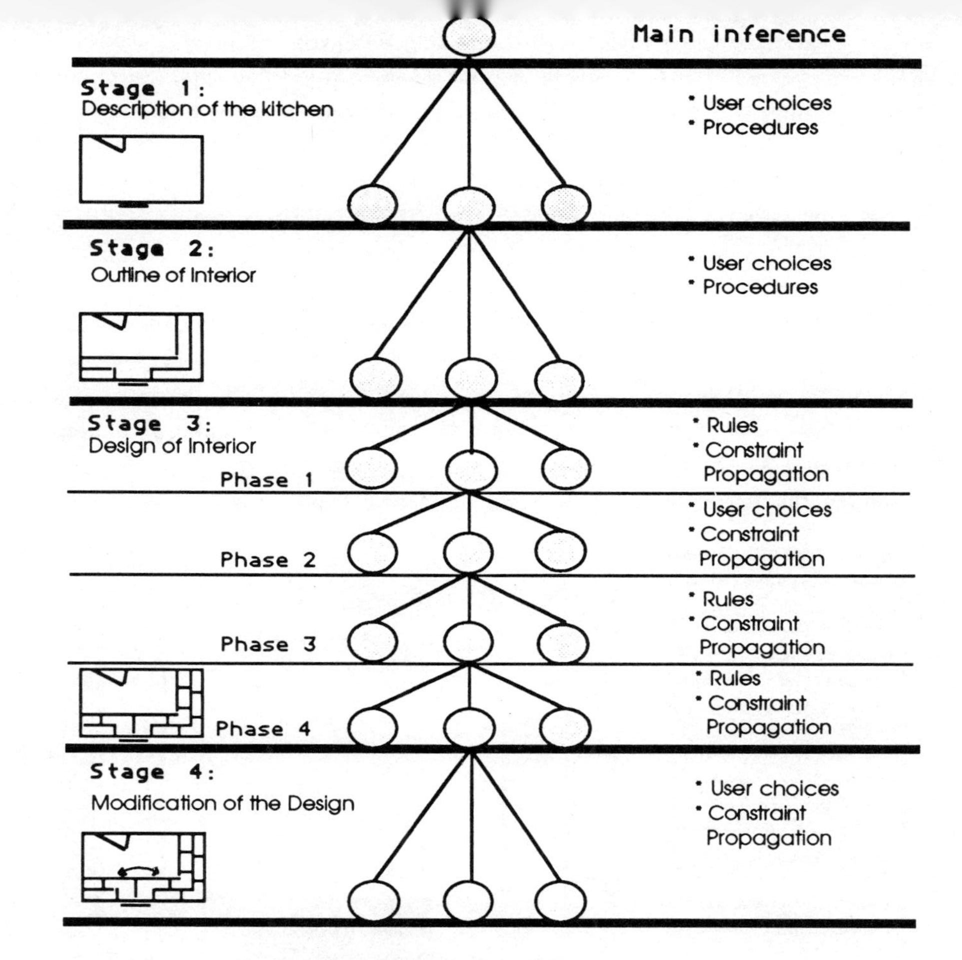

Figure 3. The solution space. Each of the stages 1, 2, 3, and 4 represents a main activity during the design process. The partial solutions resulting from each stage are visualized by the icons to the left. The inference used to get from one stage to the next is indicated to the right. The representation of each of the solution nodes at each stage is marked on the figure as well (node representation).

<u>Stage 2: Finding the Outline of the Interior</u> To find an outline of the interior, both system procedures and user choices are utilized. The outline of the interior is found as follows:

Firstly, the system finds <u>all</u> wall segments where it is allowed to place counter cabinets and wall cabinets in the kitchen, i.e. the maximum outline of interior. The system does this by checking the room constraints associated with the kitchen (from stage 1), and finds all wall segments restricted by the constraints. The maximum outline for the interior consists of all wall segments not restricted by any room constraint.

Secondly, the maximum <u>outline of interior</u> object is modified according to user specifications. A consistency check is performed on the modified outline, by going through a checklist, testing whether the interior satisfies the constraints represented in the checklist (example of such constraints: the plumbing should be included in the outline of the interior.). Backtracking is done if any of the constraints are violated.

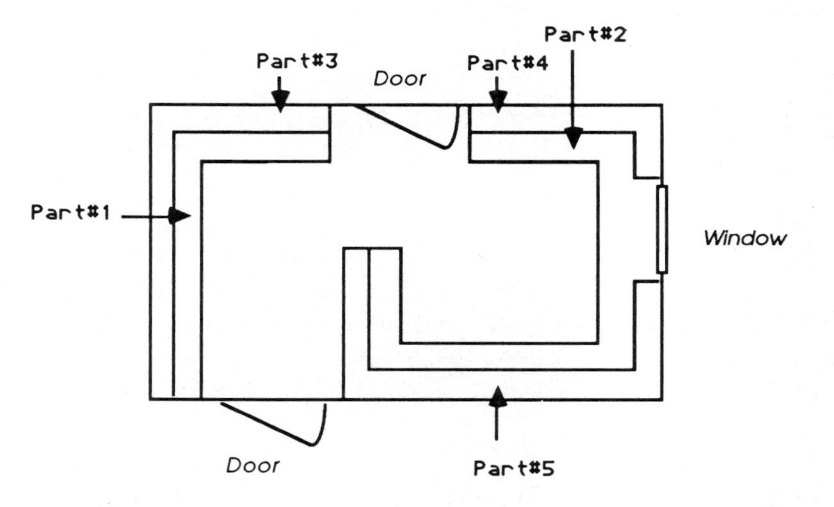

Figure 4. Visualization of the representation of an outline layout (simplified). The example outline in the figure consists of 5 parts. Part #1 and part#2 represent the outline for the counter cabinets, whereas part#3, part#4, and part#5 represent the outline for the wall cabinets. Each part consists of one or more arms, e.g., part#2 is made up of 4 arms. The peninsula is added by the user.

Solutions from this stage are represented as <u>outline of interior</u> objects. The outline layout is represented using three main types of objects. The <u>outline of the interior</u> object represents the outline as a whole, see figure 4. An outline is made up of one or more <u>parts</u>. A part is a continuous area where modules may be placed. A part is further divided into one or more <u>arms</u>, e.g. a part running along three walls consists of three arms. The three types of objects have several attributes associated with them. Some important ones are: the part-of relation between arms and parts, and between parts and the outline as a whole. Other attributes denote various geometrical and positional information about parts and arms. Examples are: the shape of a part, (e.g. L-shaped, U-shaped), an arm's position local to its part (end arm, middle arm, etc.).

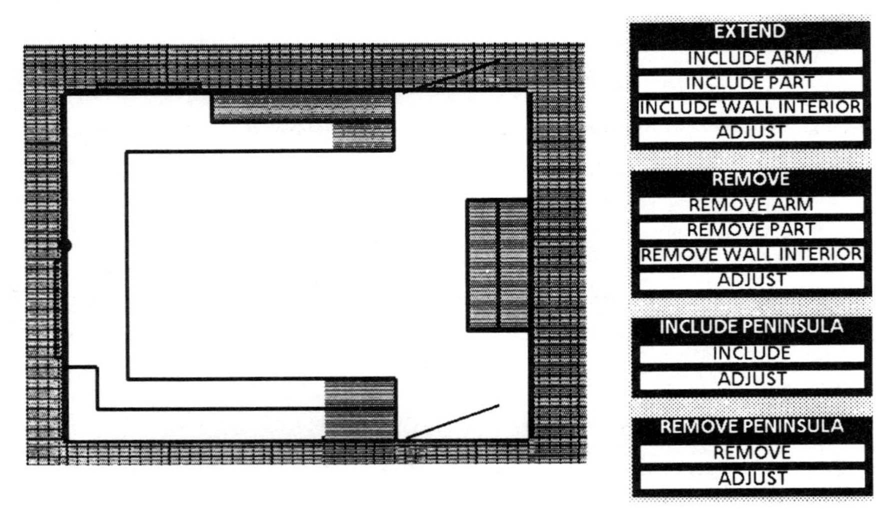

Figure 5. A screen layout showing how the user modifies the maximum outline of interior. The shaded areas are "removed" by the user, but may be reincluded if desired. Modifications (removals and extensions) are done by selecting from the menus on the right and then pointing on the figure what should be removed or included. There are 4 main functions to choose from: One may include or remove an arm, a part, everything along a wall, and do smaller adjustments, i.e., shorten an arm's length.

<u>Stage 3: Finding the Design of the Interior</u> The inference methods used in this stage include rules, constraint propagation, procedures and user choices.

The representation of the design is analogous to that of the outline, with a single exception: in the design case, <u>corners</u> are represented as separate objects apart from arms. This representation is able to capture <u>partial</u> solutions at various stages towards completion, as well as the final solution forming *Norema Design's* design suggestion to the user.

The two main types of design entities are <u>modules</u> and <u>open spaces.</u> These are the "building blocks" of a design of interior in progress, see figure 6. As figure 1 indicates, Norema's products form a natural hierarchy. Hence, in *Norema Design* modules are represented as objects organized in an IS-A taxonomy. Open spaces are represented as objects as well. A continuous open space in the outline is represented as one open space object.

As the outline of the interior is filled up with modules, the intuitive picture of a partial solution is a chain of objects linked together, every other object being a module object, the others are open space objects. A final design solution is reached when all open space objects in the chain have a width equal to 0.

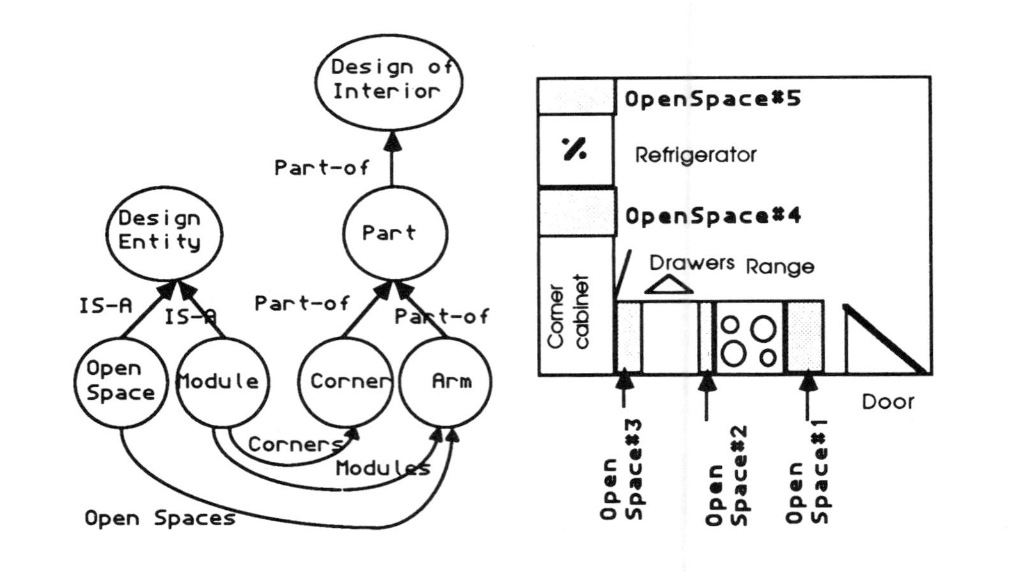

Figure 6. To the left, the objects used to represent a design of an interior. To the right, a visualization of a design solution in progress. The figure shows that a corner cabinet, the range, drawers , and the refrigerator have been placed correctly in terms of order, but not exactly in terms of of coordinates. The figure also shows the flexible length open spaces on each side of the modules.

To explain the strategy used within the design stage, we take a closer look at the kitchen design task . As stated in the definition of the kitchen design task, the selection task is the problem of deciding which modules to include in a given kitchen. In this context, any module may be classified into one of four categories:

Category 1. Modules that are to be included in every kitchen.
(e.g. range, sink cabinet, corner cabinets (if continuous interior along more than one wall))

Category 2. Modules which are included if and only if explicitly requested by the customer.
(special purpose modules, e.g. cabinet with ironing table)

Category 3. Modules whose inclusion has to be evaluated carefully by the designer in each case.

Category 4. Modules used to fill "holes" still remaining in the interior after having considered the modules in category 1-3.
(ordinary cabinets with shelves)

The configuration task requires knowledge about where a given module should be placed

- in relation to other modules
- in relation to room constraints
  (e.g. windows, doors, plumbing)
- in relation to fixed points in the kitchen interior as a whole
  (e.g. end point, corner).

In addition to the knowledge associated with the modules, it is necessary to have some procedural knowledge, that is knowledge about "what to do when" during the design process.

The classification of the modules into four categories as shown above, constitutes the basis for the strategy applied within the design stage. Thus the design stage is subdivided into the following phases (see figure 3):

Phase 1. Insert all modules in category 1 into the interior.
Phase 2. Insert all modules requested by the user (customer).
These can be taken from category 2 as well as from category 3.
Phase 3. Select modules from category 3, and insert them into the interior.
Phase 4. Select modules from category 4, and insert them into the interior.

The above enumeration of phases directly defines the order in which the modules are to be handled. The underlying ordering principle is described and motivated later in this section (see subsection Configuration of Modules). Each phase results in a partial solution represented as a design of interior object, to be further developed in the next phase. Within each phase, the solution is developed in cycles, as shown in figure 7.

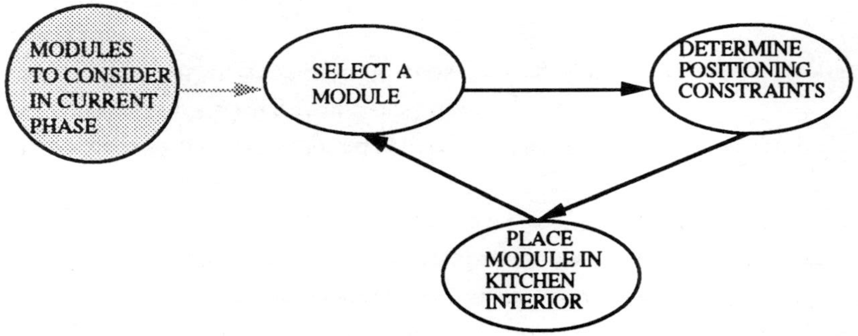

MODULES TO CONSIDER IN CURRENT PHASE
SELECT A MODULE
DETERMINE POSITIONING CONSTRAINTS
PLACE MODULE IN KITCHEN INTERIOR

Figure 7. The selection and positioning of modules within a phase.

The above figure expresses the following methodology (utilized in all phases): identify the set of modules to be considered in the current phase. The modules that are to be included in the kitchen interior are selected from this set one at a time, in the order given by the set. For each selection, the positioning constraints are determined, and the actual positioning is done, before a new module eventually is selected.

Although the main cycle described above applies to all phases, the selection task is performed quite differently in the different phases, as described next, whereas the configuration task is performed in a uniform manner throughout the design stage.

Selection of Modules In each phase the set of modules to select from has a fixed order. This ordering, which principle is described in the following section Configuration of Modules constitutes a part of the system's implicit design knowledge.

Phase 1 - Modules available in this phase are the key units of any kitchen (see category 1 above). As for range, sink and refrigerator, partial selection of these modules is done procedurally, while complete selection is based on user choice, e.g. the module RANGE is selected by a procedure, while selecting the type of range (e.g. range built into a cabinet) is up to the user. Corner cabinets are selected by rules, see example below:

IF <There are no modules of Category 1 (e.g. sink,range) in the corner> AND
<Using 90 cm from the corner along the left arm do not imply any constraint violation for the modules on left arm> AND
<Using 90 cm from the corner along the right arm do not imply any constraint violation for the modules on right arm> AND
<There are no room constraints restricting swing-out baskets 0-90 cm from the corner along the left arm> AND
<There are no room constraints restricting swing-out baskets 0-90 cm from the corner along the right arm >
THEN
<Select the 90x90 cm corner cabinet with swing-out baskets as the corner module>

Phase 2 - All selections performed in this phase are based on user choice. Consistency is checked with respect to certain requirements, e.g. "The total width of the requested modules may not exceed the total size of the free space in the outline of the interior." In case of inconsistency, the user is notified, and has the opportunity to redo choices made earlier.

Phase 3 - The modules available in this phase are a fixed ordered set of modules. Selection is here done using rules. One of the rules concerning selection of the module "wine rack" is shown below:

IF <No wine rack is included in the design of the kitchen interior> AND
<The total price of the design of the kitchen interior is not important> AND
<The size of the outline of the interior is NOT small> AND
<The total width of the open spaces of the current design ≥ 120 cm>
THEN
<Select a wine rack>

Phase 4 - Selection of the standard modules is done procedurally.

Configuration of Modules The configuration task is performed by the constraint handling mechanism, as described below.

The task, as defined in the previous chapter, involves placing the selected modules such that the constraints connected to each of them are satisfied. In this context, to position a module means to determine its position relative to the modules already included in the kitchen, not to find its absolute position. In other words, a module's position on an arm is determined only to the extent necessary to preserve the order of the modules. No modules, except the corner cabinets, have their position fixed until there is no more free space on the arm. This implies that the width of open space object between any two neighbour modules on an arm, is, according to the system's knowledge, delimited only by zero at the lower end, and at the upper end by the size of the total unoccupied (by modules) area on the arm.

Initially, all possible alternative positions are identified and ranked according to kitchen specific heuristics (rules or procedures), see example below. In this context, an alternative position is the open space between any two modules, which has a maximum extension greater than the width of the module to be inserted. Then the alternatives are investigated one by one, until a satisfactory position (open space) is found. To investigate an open space alternative for a certain module, *Norema Design* actually places the module into the open space. In terms of representation, this means to replace the open space in question with 3 objects, namely a new open space object, the module object, and another new open space object, in that order. To decide whether or not the current position (open space) is satisfactory for this particular module, the constraints connected to the module as well as the constraints connected to the modules already placed on the arm, are checked.

If no acceptable position is found by the procedure described above, there are, in general, three possible strategies to choose from:

1) Reduce the set of constraints to consider, e.g. ignore the least important constraints.
2) Give up inserting this module.
3) Backtrack, i.e. reposition the module last inserted, and try once more from there.

In *Norema Design*, backtracking in such cases proved to be very time consuming, and it did not pay off accordingly in terms of considerably increased quality of the solutions. Therefore one of the first two strategies is performed. Reducing the set of constraints is done in the phases 1 and 2 (i.e. if the module has to be included, either because it is requested by the customer, or is defined to be a necessary module). However, some of the constraints are declared to be absolute requirements. If any of these turn out to be impossible to satisfy, nothing can be done. In phase 3 (the module was originally selected by the system itself), strategy 2 is used.

At this point it is useful to study an example:

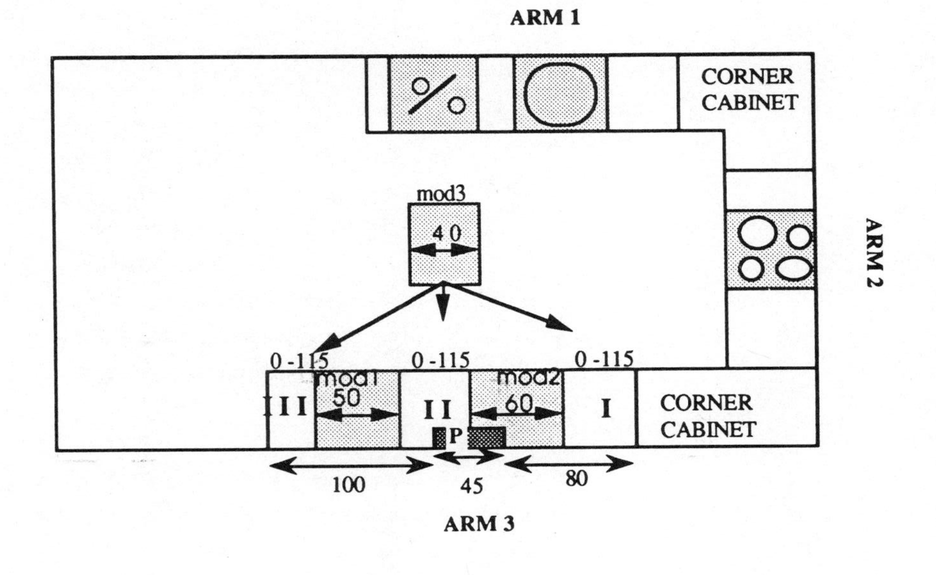

Figure 8. Visualization of a design of interior object (partial solution) during phase 2 of the Design Stage.

Consider the kitchen interior as illustrated in figure 8. P denotes a projection on the wall. Roman numerals denote the open spaces (alternative positions), whereas their widths are described by intervals given by arabic numerals. Assume the current phase is phase 2, that is the modules selected in phase 1 (range, sink, refrigerator) are already inserted, so are two of the modules (mod1 and mod2) requested by the customer. The problem at hand is to insert module mod3, also requested by the customer. Assume that mod3 is a cabinet with ironing table, which has the following (heuristic) constraints attached to it:

1. Should not be placed next to a corner.
2. Should not be placed next to the range.
3. Should not be placed next to the sink.
4. Should not be placed in front of any projection on a wall.

Constraint 4 is the only absolute requirement. According to the heuristics for cabinets with ironing table, the open spaces on arms which modules include none of the key units (range, sink and refrigerator) should be tried first. In the current case this means arm 3, which already contains two modules. Note that only the order of mod1 and mod2 is decided, not their exact position. This implies that all we know about the widths of the open spaces on arm 3 is that each has to be something between 0 cm and 115 cm, and that their sum is 115 cm, which is the size of the total free space on arm 3. Now assume that mod1 and mod2 are subject to no other constraints than constraint 4, which implies that the list above constitutes the total set of constraints necessary to take into account while trying out any alternative position on arm 3. Open space I is tried first. However, this inevitably implies violation of constraint 4 for mod2. Next to be investigated is Open space II. This time we are luckier. As mod3 is narrower than mod2, it is possible to place it in Open space II without touching the projection. As for constraint 2 and 3, neither range nor sink is situated on arm 3, so both are satisfied no matter which one of the open spaces on arm 3 is chosen. Constraint 1 is equally satisfied, as the corner cabinet keeps all other modules on arm 3 at a safe distance from the corner. Hence, placing mod3 in Open space II will satisfy constraints 1-3, and possibly satisfy constraint 4.

How Norema Design actually performs the constraint evaluations, is explained in the next few paragraphs.

The core idea in the evaluation of constraints is to regard both modules, open spaces and room constraints as one-dimensional intervals. Evaluating a certain constraint then in essence means to calculate the relation between the interval representing the module under consideration and the interval representing the object (e.g. another module) addressed by the constraint. Typical relations between intervals are overlapping and inclusion. The inspiration for this approach is taken from Vilain [11], who describes how intervals can be used to represent and reason about time. An example will clarify:

Consider the problem of evaluating the constraint "modX should not be placed in front of a window" for modX positioned somewhere in open space II, as shown in figure 9. Then the interval M defines the area spanned by all possible positions of modX (within open space II). The interval W defines the area 'occupied' by the window. m1, m2, w1, and w2 denote the end points of M and W, respectively.

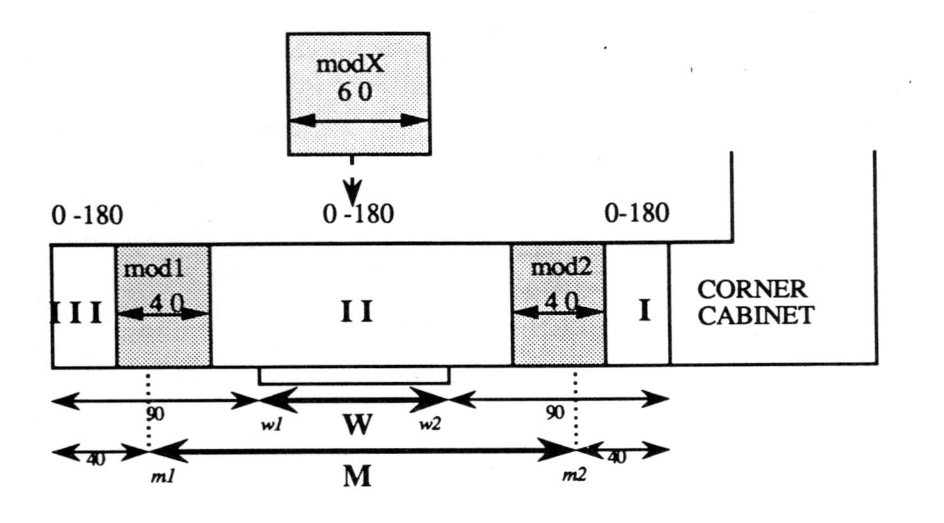

Figure 9. Visualization of the evaluation of the constraint "Module type X should not be placed in front of a window".

Now the constraint in question
is <u>necessarily satisfied</u> if and only if M do not overlap W;
is <u>possibly satisfied</u> if and only if
M overlaps W AND
(m2-w2 ≥ the width of modX OR
w1-m1 ≥ the width of modX);
is <u>necessarily not satisfied</u> if and only if
M overlaps W AND
m2-w2 < the width of modX AND
w1-m1 < the width of modX;

In the example given, the constraint is necessarily not satisfied, as the width of modX is 60, and m2-w2=50, and w1-m1=50. Hence, irrespective of <u>where</u> in open space II modX is placed, it is impossible to avoid the window.

As indicated by the example above, it is not always possible to tell if a constraint is satisfied or not. Very often the answer is unknown ("possibly satisfied"), because the extension of the position alternative (open space) in question is not sufficiently delimited at the time of evaluation. The principle followed in *Norema Design* is that <u>any constraint is satisfied until proven violated</u>. In general, this approach may in some cases lead to an impossible constellation, i.e. at some stage in the design process it may prove impossible to satisfy all of the absolute requirements. This may not be discovered until the last module on the arm is to be inserted.

It is important to minimize the frequency of such situations, and thereby minimize the need for taking actions as earlier explained (backtrack, relax some constraints or desist from inserting the module). In *Norema Design* this is handled by giving <u>the order</u> in which the modules are inserted into the kitchen interior a careful consideration. Three main principles are put to work:

- any module whose position depends on the position of another module, should be inserted after the module it depends on.
- modules with strong positioning constraints attached to them, should be inserted before modules underlying weaker constraints.
- modules that necessarily have to be included (e.g. because of customer request) should be inserted before any other modules are considered.

To summarize the design stage, the following points should be observed:

Heuristics *Norema Design* uses kitchen specific heuristics both at micro-level (within the single rule or constraint), and at a higher level, e.g. in ordering the alternative positions to be tried when placing a module. Besides the structure of the design process itself is based on domain specific heuristics.

Relaxation of Positioning Requirements When designing difficult kitchens, it is often not possible to satisfy all the positioning constraints that apply to the situation. *Norema Design* is fairly adaptive to such cases, as it has the ability to ignore constraints of minor importance. Whether or not this ability is used, depends, as we have seen, on how important it is to include the module.

Evaluation of Constraints It should be pointed out that the constraint evaluation function is three-valued, that is, the value of the function is either True, False or Unknown. There is no mechanism to discover when a constraint is <u>almost</u> satisfied. Using fuzzy logic would probably entail a significant enhancement in this respect.

Stage 4: Modification of the Design

The user may modify the system's design suggestion by moving, removing, inserting, interchanging, or exchanging a module with another module in the solution. During this process, *Norema Design* will act as a critic, telling the user if a modification to the design violates any design rules (only the most important ones). Hence, both tasks (selection and configuration) are based on user choice. To preserve consistency throughout the modification stage, constraint propagation is performed to check user choices.

The solution resulting from this stage is a design of interior object, representing the final design of the kitchen, as it appears after modification of the system's suggestion derived in stage 3.

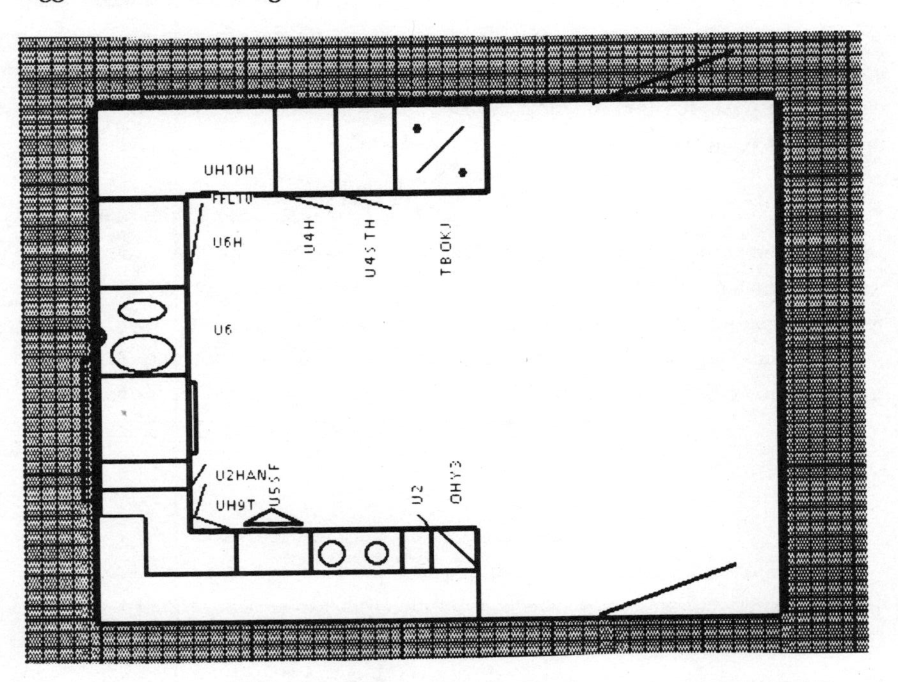

Figure 10. A screen image showing a kitchen design designed by Norema Design. Only the counter cabinets are configured on the figure. The codes shown by the modules are Norema's ordering codes.

DISCUSSIONS AND CONCLUSIONS

Solutions

The way Norema Design performs the design process, does not necessarily lead to an optimal solution (the term 'optimal' is here to be understood as optimal in relation to the (after all) incomplete knowledge stored in the system, as opposed to true optimality, which would be a measure for the value or quality of a solution seen with the eyes of the customer).

In the course of positioning a module, the system stops as soon as a (probably) acceptable position is found, rather than trying more alternatives and comparing the results to end up with the best (according to its knowledge).

The chief argument for this method is of course efficiency. Besides, kitchen design is, like most types of design, a subjective matter; often there is no "right or wrong"; decisions are based partly on own preferences, creativity, and experience. As a result of this, there is no generally optimal way to design the layout for a kitchen. The knowledge in the system is a combination of the acquired knowledge from the two design experts. The main role of the system is to produce functionally good layouts. The layouts may be characterized as standard solutions as opposed to "fancy" and creative solutions. It is up to the user herself to give the design a "personal touch" by modifying the system's suggestion to fit her own personal taste and needs. The system's suggestion is meant to serve as a good starting point for the inexperienced designer.

Problems and Experiences

Different kinds of problems are associated with software development and the development of expert systems is certainly no exception to this. Our problems are mostly related to the size of the application, which is now becoming quite large. This has had the following consequences:

System Efficiency As *Norema Design* is going to be used as a tool for a salesperson while assisting a customer, the response time of the system is of great importance. Concerning the time needed to produce a design of a given outline of an interior, 5 minutes or less is considered to be acceptable. This is not a very strict requirement. Nonetheless, although *Norema Design* currently has been run in interpreted mode, and a performance gain of order of 5-10 can be expected through compilation, at a certain point it was quite clear that the response time would reach a figure which was too high. We therefore found it necessary to restructure the knowledge base. This involved a change in representation of the configuration knowledge, from rules to a more explicit representation included as a part of the data structure. In addition to improving the transparency of the configuration knowledge and reduce the size of the knowledge base, these changes will probably result in an increased efficiency gain from compilation , as performance gain through compilation is larger for functions than for rules.

Runtime Cost *Norema Design* will run on PCs located at Norema's retail stores. The application requires 7-8 MByte of prime memory on such a PC. The necessary memory extension will lead to a relatively large expense for the retailers.

Development Efficiency In addition to the very common problem of execution efficiency, we have met some unexpected problems indirectly caused by the size of the application. It turned out that certain limitations in Xerox's software is not properly handled in Epitool, the most severe of which has to do with the garbage collector. This problem is in fact a continuous cause of frustration, especially as it complicates testing of the program. It has been indicated that later versions of Epitool will not cause these kinds of problems, though.

Extension of Problem Domain and Applicability

Norema supports products and fittings for both home furnishing and furnishing of commercial buildings. An extension of the problem domain is therefore possible. Beside kitchen design, the design of bathroom and wardrobe floorplans is of interest as far as home furnishing is concerned. The use of a design system for banks, offices, shops etc. also seems appropriate, and these would represent a further extension of the problem domain.

The users of *Norema Design* are primarily kitchen sales staff, inexperienced in designing kitchen floorplans. Most of these vendors are not employed by Norema Ltd, however. Norema's strategy is now to train their own sales staff. *Norema Design* could be a system for this purpose, by adding an explanation facility. The system would then be able to both criticize the designers' actions, and to explain how and why it reached a kitchen floorplan. In this way it could be a tutor for novice designers.

Acknowledgements

The Norema Design project has since 1987 been partly financed by the Royal Norwegian Council for Scientific and Industrial Research (NTNF), and thanks are due to them for making this possible.

REFERENCES

1. Cathain, C. O. (1987). Expert Systems and Design. *Design studies* **8**(2).

2. Eastman, C. M. (1973). Automated Space Planning. *Artificial Intelligence* **4**.

3. Epitec A.B. (1987). Epitool Development Tool. Reference manual.

4. Fawcett, W. (1987). A note on the logic of design. *Design Studies* **8**(2).

5. Fischer, G. and Morch,A. (1988). CRACK: A Critiquing Approach to Cooperative Kitchen Design. University of Colorado, Boulder.

6. Fox, M. and Baykan, C. A. (1988). Wright; an Intelligent CAD System. Draft. Carnegie-Mellon University, Pittsburg .

7. Frayman, F. and Mittal, S. (1987). COSSACK: A Constraint-Based Expert System for Configuration Tasks, *in* Sriram, D. and Adey, R. A. (eds.). *Knowledge Based Expert Systems in Engineering: Planning and Design*. Computational Mechanics Publications, Ashurst, pp. 143-166.

8. McDermott, J. (1982). R1. A Rule-Based Configurer of Computer Systems. *Artificial Intelligence* **19**(1).

9. Magee, K. (1987). The Elicitation of Knowledge from Designers. *Design Studies* **8**(2).

10. Oxman, R. and Gero, J. S. (1987). Using an Expert System for Design Diagnosis and design Synthesis. *Expert Systems* **4**(1).

11. Vilain, M.B. (1982). A system for reasoning about time, *in* The National Conference on Artificial Intelligence, Pittsburgh, Penn. *Proceedings*, pp.197-201.

From *Advances in Engineering Software* Conference Proceedings, 1985

AN EXPERT SYSTEM FOR PRELIMINARY NUMERICAL DESIGN-MODELLING

K. J. MacCallum and A. Duffy
Department of Ship and Marine Technology, University of Strathclyde, Glasgow

1 Introduction

From the earliest days of Computer Aided Design (CAD) there has been a clear recognition that establishing effective communication between the computer and the designer is crucial to the development of a productive design system. Early papers on the philosophy and concepts of CAD stated quite clearly that man and machine had to work together in a co-operative environment; and a few systems were developed to show the potential of this kind of approach. A fine example of the appreciation of this potential is given in a paper by Robert Mann and Steve Coons in 1965 [1]. In this paper, they state: "It is clear that what is needed if the computer is to be of greater use in the creative process, is a more intimate and continuous interchange between man and machine. This interchange must be of such a nature that all forms of thought that are congenial to man, whether verbal, symbolic, numerical, or even graphical are also understood by the machine and are acted upon by the machine in ways that are appropriate to man's purpose." The emphasis on the computer's understanding of man's purpose and on communication at the level of thought are significant.

Despite the early suggestions, an examination of developments in CAD systems leads to the conclusion that the greatest advances in the application of computers to engineering design have been the assistance in 'number crunching' for design analysis, and the development of specialized systems for limited design tasks. Parallel improvements in man–machine communication have been achieved through improved availability and accessibility of computing power and significant advances in computer graphics, providing a more acceptable medium for exchange of information. However, even those advances have not made significant inroads into the problems of advanced communication. Only recently with increasing emphasis on product modelling has there been a gradual awareness that CAD systems require a much deeper level of user knowledge and problem knowledge than is currently normal. It would seem, therefore, that much of the early potential of CAD has not yet been realised.

The work described in this paper addresses itself to this goal. It is argued that progress towards the goal can only be made by building into design systems a greater understanding of man's purpose. The key to this is to build systems which have explicit knowledge and are able to manipulate that knowledge and reason with it. The concept of 'expert systems' is built on this approach. This paper describes a system called DESIGNER which is an expert system concerned with building and handling knowledge of numerical relationships in preliminary design. The system is illustrated and evaluated using examples from preliminary ship design.

2 The nature of the design process

Before looking at ways of representing design knowledge, it is worthwhile examining the design process itself in order to understand what contribution we can expect computers to make. A key characteristic of much of engineering design is the complexity of the objects or systems of interest. Typically, a system will have many components, each of which will be related in different ways to other components through their characteristics. A designer's task is to create a specification for such a system, given a set of required functional objectives to be achieved in a given environment. The designer will rely on measures of performance, both objective and subjective, to select the most promising concepts for evaluation. However, complexity prevents the designer evaluating all concepts in detail; instead the design is broken down into parts and each part is tackled in a number of stages corresponding to levels of detail. Earlier stages have the least detail and use only the parameters which have the greatest influence on the overall design performance, whereas later stages operate within the constraints of previously defined parameters. A crucial feature of this approach is that individual stages are more tractable because the numbers of independent parameters and their interactions are reduced.

A conclusion which can be drawn from this brief description of the design process is that a designer's first expressions of concepts are in terms of objects, their characteristics, and the relationships which exist among them. One way of viewing design is as a process of modelling in which the above expressions constitute the model. Thus in every situation the designer creates some kind of abstract model which simulates some aspect of the behaviour of the thing being designed. In fact it is likely that, for each concept, the designer handles a variety of models simultaneously, each one representing a different abstraction, but being consistent with the others. The models are essentially mental models but will be formalised through graphical, numerical, logical, and physical means. The creation of a model, which is a process of synthesis, is difficult to formalise. Evaluation of a particular model, however, is a process of analysis. It requires effort and sometimes ingenuity; but in most cases the procedures of evaluation are well defined. The overall design process involves establishing and collecting a variety of models, interchanging synthesis and analysis, and allowing interaction between design objectives and model specifications [2].

In summary it is useful to identify some important characteristics of the design process:

(a) *creative* — it requires imagination and inventiveness to build conceptual models. As a result of creative activities, the form and structure of these models may change or develop as the design proceeds.

(b) *multiple solutions* — there can be many answers to a given design problem, all of which may achieve the objectives, and may thus be technically and economically feasible. Thus the design process is not deterministic.

(c) *empirical* — the process of creating and evaluating a model does not always follow well formalised rules with good theoretical bases. Very often relationships are of an empirical nature.

(d) *approximate* — because design is a modelling process which uses empirical relationships, the results obtained are generally approximate. Accuracy increases as the design proceeds and greater levels of detail are included. However, the concepts of expected and acceptable accuracy are important to the designer.

(e) *requires expertise* — the designer uses his expertise in many different ways during design, with respect to relationships used, the actual design process, and even in the judgement of the acceptability of proposed solutions.

These characteristics are most in evidence at the creative or preliminary stages of design during which basic concepts are being developed. However, the same characteristics are the ones which in many senses are the most difficult to computerise, involving intuition, experience, approximation and empiricism. It is hardly surprising, therefore, that conventional approaches of CAD to the creative stage of design have had limited success.

3 Expert systems approach

One of the most promising developments in the use of computers in recent years has been the work on expert systems [3]. Its significance is that it addresses itself to providing computer systems which are able to make a 'knowledgeable' contribution to complex problems in a specific domain or field of interest; that is, to act as an 'expert'. A human expert is someone who has a specialised body of knowledge and is able to apply it to solve problems, to advise, to act as a consultant, and to communicate his knowledge with others. An expert system is a computer system which is able to enact a similar role. The major advance of expert systems compared to more conventional software systems is the explicit representation and manipulation of a body of knowledge. The 'knowledge base' can be used by the system in solving problems, in its own area of relevance, and can be added to directly by the human expert or by the system itself.

There are several important features in expert systems which make them capable of tackling problems of great complexity. The first of these is a description and representation of knowledge in some formalised language. This immediately makes the knowledge base available and understandable to its users, and allows experts to examine and modify the system's knowledge as new situations are encountered. The second important feature is the system's ability to reason using a combination of known facts and generalised relationships in the knowledge base. Because the reasoning mechanisms and their control can be structured separately from the knowledge base it is easier to express problems for solution. A third feature is the system's ability to provide explanations of the steps taken to reach a conclusion. This follows naturally from the formalised representation of the knowledge.

While many simple expert systems have used the knowledge representation and control techniques adopted in earlier successful research work [4], there are still many areas of concern for the longer-term development of expert systems. Some of these are the representations for new types of knowledge such as common-sense knowledge and uncertainty, required depth of knowledge, control over the use of knowledge, and the use of logic systems.

Michie [3] has identified three different user modes for an expert system in contrast to the single mode (getting answers to a problem) typical of the more familiar type of computing:

(a) *user as a client* — system acts as a consultant from whom the user wishes to get answers to problems.

(b) *user as a tutor* — system accepts instructions from a domain specialist to improve or refine its knowledge.

(c) *user as a pupil* — system can use its expert knowledge to instruct users in certain approaches.

To these three modes it is probably useful to add a fourth:

(d) *user as an assistant* — system interacts with user to encourage user to find a solution to a problem with guidance, advice and stimulation from the system.

It is this last mode which is most relevant to the design situation. The work described in this paper is based on the contention that the approaches being taken in expert systems provide a key to realising the potential of CAD. For many years now we have been building complex CAD systems which contain increasing amounts of knowledge. However, that knowledge has been highly constrained to particular methods, and has been implicitly rather than explicitly available. Systems based on ideas of explicit knowledge representation and reasoning, offer the possibility of greater productivity in the contribution they make to man-machine communication.

4 A design assistant for numerical design

From the discussion of the previous section it is concluded that any system which intends to take a more active role in a design dialogue must have the following features:

- a powerful semantically rich interface
- a highly flexible design modelling and modification system
- an understanding (at least superficially) of design concepts and goals
- a capability for abstraction
- a method of capturing and using expertise in a useful way
- an ability to explain its own reasoning processes.

While we are still some way from achieving all these features, they indicate the direction of recent design system trends.

This section describes an approach to creating a design assistant for numerical design based on this philosophy. The system, called DESIGNER, was constructed to meet the following requirements:

(a) flexible representation of user's design models;

(b) ability to modify models, adding new design parameters or relationships, during the design process;

(c) ability to represent designer's expertise with respect to numerical modelling;

(d) provide feedback to the designer on the nature of relationships implied by a model; and

(e) variety of levels of control of the design process by the designer.

The requirements place emphasis on providing adequate knowledge representations and control rather than on the user interface. Thus the system will be described in terms of its knowledge structure before providing methods and examples of use.

4.1 A network model of design

To define and illustrate the role of relationships in the numerical design process, it is valuable to have a more formalised way of presenting models. DESIGNER presents a model as a directed network. In such a network, the various nodes represent the characteristics of interest, and a link between two nodes represents a dependency as contained in some relationship, the direction of the dependency being shown by an arrowhead. Thus Figure 1 shows that the volume of a box depends on its length, its breadth, and its depth. The three dependencies together are contained in a single relationship:

$$\text{volume} = \text{length} \times \text{breadth} \times \text{depth}$$

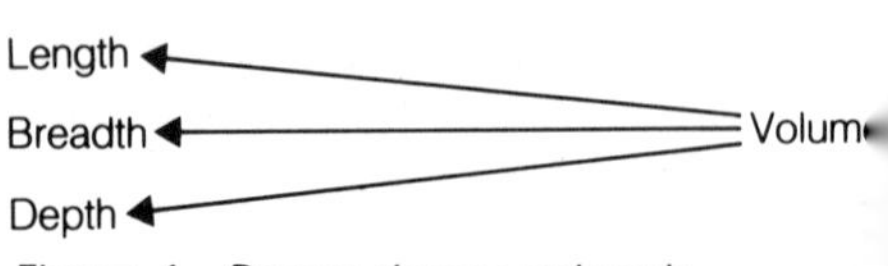

Figure 1 Dependency network

which allows volume to be calculated from these three characteristics. A more realistic example, which represents a simplified preliminary stage of ship design is shown in Figure 2.

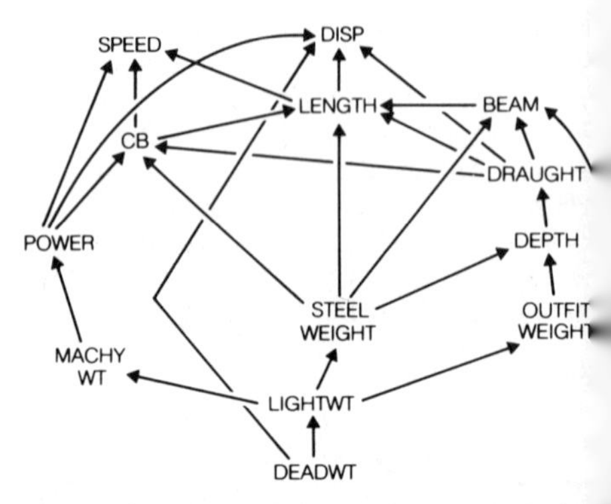

Figure 2 Network for preliminary desig

veral important points can be made in eneral about the approach of network odelling:

) While some relationships are fixed in their form, either because they follow physical laws or they are defined by legislative requirements, many design relationships are of an empirical nature. Thus the results of using such relationships can only be considered to be approximately correct.

) Again because of the empirical nature of numerical design, a particular characteristic may have a number of valid relationships for estimating a value. The choice of which relationship to use in a particular situation will be related to particular contexts, degree of detail being considered, availability of other information, and other expertise.

) The network model can be considered to represent the network of currently active relationships. Thus the model can change with the progress of design.

) In Figure 1, if the volume depends on the length, then length can be considered to influence volume, i.e. a change in the value of length will affect the value of volume. Thus the inverse of the dependency network is an influence network. The effect of any characteristic on another can be determined by tracing through all the intermediate paths in the network.

) Some relationships may need to be used in a number of different forms depending on a designer's approach to a problem. For example, in Figure 1 it would be just as correct in some situations to redraw it so that length is dependent on volume, breadth and depth.

conclusion, the directed network is a seful way of modelling numerical esign. However, it rapidly becomes omplex to visualise, and can only ustrate an active network within a uch more detailed network.

2 The characteristic frame

nowledge about a characteristic is ncapsulated in a 'frame' of knowledge, at is a formalised structure containing levant information in 'slots' (Figure 3).

The main items of knowledge which re available to the user through his ctions are:

) *a name* — by which the characteristic can be referenced;

) *an explanation* — an extended name which can be used for fuller explanations or for more complex referencing;

) *a current value* — representing the latest answer calculated for this characteristic truncated to a value consistent with the known accuracy of the calculated value. A value may be 'unknown';

(d) *accuracy* — a measure of the accuracy of the value calculated, expressed as a likely error in the value;

(e) *units* — the units in which the value has been measured;

(f) *relationships* — a set of numerical relationships, any of which could be valid for estimating a value. Each relationship in turn contains a list of dependent characteristics, the actual relationship, a list of conditions which have to be satisfied before the relationship is considered valid, and a list of conditions which have to be satisfied before the characteristic is updated with the generated value. Each relationship also has associated with it a reliability.

(g) *influences* — a list of characteristics which this characteristic is known to influence with the currently active network. Associated with these influences is a 'strength' indicating the degree of influence. Strength is equivalent to a numerical derivative.

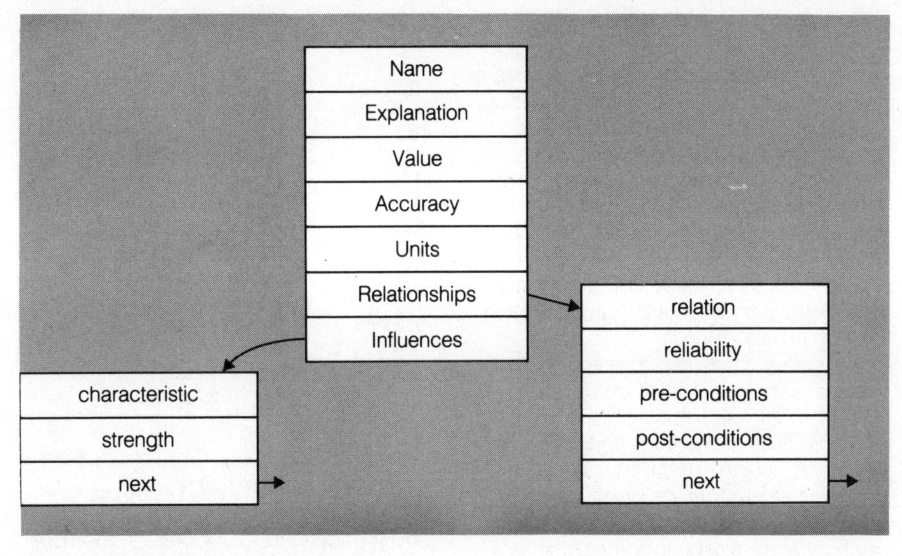

Figure 3 Characteristic frame

4.3 The DESIGNER system

The network model and the characteristic frame together describe the underlying structure of DESIGNER. Superimposed on that structure are mechanisms to control the use and propagation of characteristic values and relationships, and a user interface which allows the designer to express his model, his expertise, his goals and his control over the design process.

A user would normally expect to start a particular problem with a set of characteristics and for each, a list of relationships available. He may then decide to provide some parameter values he knows, or simply to ask for an 'estimate' of values for some performance variables. As he proceeds through evaluations of the model, he may add new relationships together with conditions under which it is appropriate to use them. At any point, the system will provide information on the strength of influence between any pair of characteristics. Eventually the user will feel that he has reached a situation which meets his goals to some acceptable degree of confidence and will move to a more detailed stage of design.

Two basic actions taken when using DESIGNER are ESTIMATE and UPDATE. ESTIMATE is used to obtain a value for a characteristic from known values of other characteristics using a valid relationship. Where a relationship requires a characteristic value which is not available, one of two things happen; either the system asks the user to provide a value, or if an automatic search mode has been set, the system calls ESTIMATE recursively until all values are resolved. There is an important side-effect of using ESTIMATE. Every time a relationship is used, each of the input characteristics can 'learn' something about its own role in the network. In particular it learns of one other characteristic which it directly influences and the strength of that influence. This learning process is the basis of the system creating an influence network.

Each time ESTIMATE is used, the system has to find a valid relationship. In practice a single characteristic may have a number of relationships which are valid in a particular context. In this case the system selects the relationship which has the highest reliability measure. It is open to the user when asked for a value for a characteristic to respond 'UNKNOWN'. The implication of this is that the recursive list of relationships which are depending on this value fail and some alternative relationships, perhaps of lower reliability, need to be tried.

The UPDATE operation is used to allocate a known value to a particular characteristic. In addition to updating a value, it uses its knowledge of influences to do two things; first it traces through the influence network to mark all influenced values as inconsistent, and secondly it warns the user of the immediate effects of his action. If the system is in automatic propagation mode, then it will follow through all the implications of these influences, calling UPDATE recursively.

The system is always able to provide the user with information about the current model structure, and a characteristic knowledge including its influences. At any stage the user can determine the strength of influence of one parameter on another, the system using its knowledge of immediate influence strengths to derive these. In addition, the system can explain how values have been derived, identifying the relationships which were successfully selected, and the characteristic values used in their evaluation.

Throughout the evaluation process of a network model, the system maintains a concept of approximation of derived values. Inaccuracy in a derived value is expressed to the user as a value ± tolerance. In general, inaccuracy in a value depends on the reliability of a relationship used, and the tolerances which already exist on the dependent characteristic values. Those inaccuracies can be propagated through the network in a manner similar to strengths, providing the user with soundly based measures of the degree of approximation in results obtained.

5 Examples of use

To illustrate DESIGNER and the features just described, a simplified preliminary ship design problem will be considered. The design model is similar to that shown in Figure 2, but to be more realistic, it includes a number of multiple relationships. Table 1 summarises the main parameters included in the model, and the number of relationships which have been defined for each model. The objective of the design process is to select a set of values for the main dimensions (L, B, T, D and CB) such that it meets requirements of deadweight (DWT) and speed (V). Simple empirical relationships have been taken from published sources to create this basic model. For the purposes of the example, the requirements are taken as a deadweight (or payload) of 22 300 tonnes and a trial speed of 14 knots. The designer as a first step assumes that a reasonable value of displacement is 26 000 tonnes and of beam/draught ratio is 2.4. He then inputs to the system:

Update V with 14
Update BT with 2.4
Update DISP with 26 000
Estimate DWT

Table 1 Key parameters and number of relationships

Symbol	*Explanation*	*No. of relationships*
B	moulded beam	4
BT	beam/draft ratio	1
CB	block coefficient	2
D	moulded depth	3
DISP	moulded displacement	1
DWT	full deadweight	1
GM	initial stability	1
L	L_{BP}	4
POWER	shaft power	1
T	draught	3
V	trial speed	0
WEIGHTS	lightship mass	1

The system responds to the Estimate by recursively searching for valid relationships for which information is known or can be supplied by the user, producing as it goes the following set of values:

```
L          143.35 m
CB           0.80
T            9.60 m
B           23.05 m
D           13.54 m
POWER     7351   kW
WEIGHTS   5201   tonnes
DWT      20799   tonnes
```

The system's explanation of how these values were derived shows the specific relationships which were used. Alternatively, the system could be required to print-out its search process as it goes along. An extract from this is given below:

```
B  ESTIMATE
  PHYS BEING TRIED
      B DEPENDS ON [DISP  L  T  CB]
T  ESTIMATE
  PHYS BEING TRIED
      T DEPENDS ON [DISP  L  B  CB]
      B CURRENTLY BEING ESTIMATED
      THIS RELATIONSHIP NOT SUITABLE
  SOLVE BEING TRIED
      T DEPENDS ON [DISP  L  BT  CB]
CB  ESTIMATE
      EMP BEING TRIED
          CB DEPENDS ON [V                    L]
ESTIMATE    OF   CB   IS    0.80
            OF   T    IS    9.60
            OF   B    IS   23.05
```

It is worthwhile noting in this case the failure of valid relationships because of lack of information, followed by an attempt with an alternative relationship. The names of the relationships being tried have been provided during the definition of the model.

The overall result from this first estimate is that the deadweight is too low by about 1500 tonnes. Using the strengths feature, the system reveals that an increase in deadweight of about 1500 tonnes could be achieved by increasing DISP by about 1750 tonnes. The effect of changing beam/draught ratio is negligible. Thus DISP can be 'UPDATED' to 27700. Normally the system will respond by warning the user of the immediate influences of this update; in this case:

The following will be affected by DISP

Deadweight
B
T
L

If the automatic propagation mode was set then these immediate influences would be followed through, making the remainder of the network consistent. Alternatively, the user can again ask for deadweight to be estimated. In this case the overall effect will be the same and a value of deadweight of 22 258 tonnes is produced.

As yet no unreliabilities have been nentioned, even though they should be associated with the relationships being used. If these are included using data from a range of available vessels then the latest set of values printed out would have read:

L	146.41 ± 4.39 m
CB	0.80 ± 0.02
T	9.79 ± 0.21 m
B	23.50 ± 1.11 m
D	13.81 ± 0.75 m
POWER	7652 ± 1056 kW
WEIGHTS	5442 ± 668 tonnes
DWT	22258 ± 668 tonnes

With this level of approximation in the elationships, the deadweight equirement is well within the bounds of the answer.

The design process continues with an estimate of stability (GM). The value of .69 ± 0.93 m is unsatisfactory and so urther changes are required. The designer finds from the system that beam/draught ratio, and beam and draught themselves are the parameters which most influence GM. However, he eels that beam should not increase and hus decides to achieve his requirements of GM by changing draught, and keep is deadweight requirement by hanging Length. The final set of values :

L	151.32 m
CB	0.81 ± 0.02
T	9.50 m
B	23.50 m
D	13.39 ± 0.67 m
POWER	7731 ± 1033 kW
WEIGHTS	5629 ± 658 tonnes
DWT	22288 ± 658 tonnes
GM	1.95 ± 0.92

is of interest to note that this last equence of operations changed the dependent variables from eam/draught ratio and displacement length, beam and draught. Thus the lationships used and consequently the etwork of dependencies and influences as changed. A second point of note is at a change now to one of the dependent variables in automatic opagation mode would result in both eadweight and GM being updated. is is now a different effect from just 'estimating' deadweight, which would leave GM as inconsistent.

6 Discussion

This paper has been concerned with presenting an overall knowledge-based approach to handling numerical relationships in the preliminary stages of design. The last section illustrated the system by stepping through a simple ship design example. A number of features of the system were not presented since the aim was simply to convey the 'flavour' of the system and to illustrate the overall concepts involved. However, it is worth emphasising a number of points with respect to the DESIGNER system and the examples used:

(a) There is complete flexibility to set up large varieties of design models; i.e. there is nothing in the DESIGNER system which is related specifically to ship design.

(b) The user of the system has a large degree of control over the process of design, both in terms of the sequence of steps and the rate of progress.

(c) In defining the model for the example, there were no assumptions made about what information would be available; neither were there assumptions about the way the user would approach the design process.

(d) The system uses built-in expertise to look for suitable relationships. Thus, only a part of the total model definition is active at one time.

(e) The system learns about influences and strengths of influence through the use of the model. The results of this can be used to provide guidance to the user about possible solution areas.

Despite the achievements of the system in taking a step toward a more knowledgeable design assistant, there are a number of areas in which research is still required:

(a) The present system deals only with numerical relationships. The other major aspect in any early design considerations is spatial arrangement. Although the present system allows graphical output of design trends or geometric representations, it cannot be considered to 'know' about spatial arrangements in the same way that it knows about characteristics.

(b) The major focus of attention has been to provide a flexible and rich set of facilities for handling numerical design problems. Little attention has been given to providing the most effective interface for handling this knowledge-based system.

(c) Because of the complexity of the system, careful study needs to be given to providing the correct level of communication between the human designer and the DESIGNER system. This is more than just an interface problem; it implies a deeper modelling of the user and the system.

(d) Any long-term accumulation of expertise by the system relies on relationships provided by designers. There should be links to design data bases which would allow relationships to be extracted and added to the system.

7 Conclusions

It has been stated that CAD still has considerable potential for advancing the process of design, and that recent developments in expert systems and knowledge-based systems currently hold the key to releasing some of that potential.

A system, called DESIGNER which is based on these developments has been presented. This demonstrates a number of features which are normally difficult to achieve in more conventional CAD systems. However, there are clearly many areas which require further research and development.

References

1 Mann, R. W. and Coons, S. A. (1965) 'Computer Aided Design' *McGraw-Hill Yearbook — Science and Technology*, McGraw-Hill

2 Malhotra, A., Thomas, J. C., Carroll, J. M. and Miller, L. A. (1980) 'Cognitive processes in design' *Int. J. Man-Machine Studies* No. 12

3 Michie, D. (1980) 'Expert systems' *Computer Journal* Vol. 23, No. 4

4 Alty, J. L. and Coombs, M. J. (1984) *Expert Systems — Concepts and Examples* NCC Publications